Time-Savers for Teachers

SPELLING YEARS 5-6

Peter Clutterbuck

W
FRANKLIN WATTS
LONDON • SYDNEY

How to use this book

This book provides a range of worksheets suitable for children in Years 5 and 6 of primary school. The worksheets are grouped into sections that correspond to the word level work specified in the National Literacy Strategy. The contents are equally relevant to the Scottish 5–14 Guidelines, and the curricula for the Republic and Northern Ireland.

Each section starts with an *introduction* that sets the topic in context. The worksheets that follow cater for *different* levels of ability. Complete *answers* are provided to save time with marking. You can then keep the worksheets as part of the pupils' *assessment* records.

All teacher-pages have a vertical stripe down the side of the page. All the worksheets are photocopiable.

This edition first published
in Great Britain in 2004

Franklin Watts
96 Leonard Street
London EC2A 4XD

Worksheets copyright © Blake Education
Teachers' notes copyright © Franklin Watts 2004

UK edition adapted by Brenda Stones,
with teachers' assistance from
Sarah St John (in Merton and Ealing)
and Jo Owston (in Finchley and Devon).

This edition not for sale outside
the United Kingdom and Eire

ISBN 0 7496 5803 7

Printed in Dubai

Contents

Medium frequency words to be taught through Year 5

National Literacy Strategy Framework

Year 5

Term 1:

baby, balloon, birthday, brother, children, clothes, garden, great, happy, head, heard, something, sure, swimming, those, word, work, world.

Term 2:

earth, eyes, father, friends, important, lady, light, money, mother, own, paper, sister, small, sound, white, whole, why, window.

Term 3:

Use this term to check up on spelling knowledge from previous terms.

The complete list for Years 4–5

above	don't	morning	think
across	during	mother	those
almost	earth	much	thought
along	every	near	through
also	eyes	never	today
always	father	number	together
animal	first	often	told
any	follow(ing)	only	tries
around	found	opened	turn(ed)
asked	friends	other	under
baby	garden	outside	until
balloon	goes	own	upon
before	gone	paper	used
began	great	place	walk(ed)(ing)
being	half	right	watch
below	happy	round	where
better	head	second	while
between	heard	show	white
birthday	high	sister	whole
both	I'm	small	why
brother	important	something	window
brought	inside	sometimes	without
can't	jumped	sound	woke(n)
change	knew	started	word
children	know	still	work
clothes	lady	stopped	world
coming	leave	such	write
didn't	light	suddenly	year
different	might	sure	young
does	money	swimming	

Introduction to Consonant Clusters

Even though consonant clusters are first taught in Year 1, they are still worth practising in ever more complex vocabulary.

If children can distinguish and discriminate between different initial blended sounds, it will help them get started on the spelling, and help them search for the word in the dictionary.

Consonant Clusters

Name _____

1. **Use each sp word to complete a sentence.**

sparrow	sport	spine	spring
splinter	sponge	spider	spade

a. I dug the hole in the ground using a _____.

b. A _____ is a small bird.

c. Cricket is a popular _____.

d. Your _____ is made up of a number of bones.

e. Mike got a _____ in his finger.

f. In _____ the trees begin to grow new leaves.

g. A _____ is a small creature with eight legs.

h. I used a _____ to clean myself in the bath last night.

2. **Complete each word.**

Use these.

gl	sk	sc	pr	cr	fl	fr	cl

a. ___ ___ipping

b. ___ ___rew

c. ___ ___ison

d. ___ ___uit

e. ___ ___asses

f. ___ ___oak

g. ___ ___eece

h. ___ ___ane

3. **Find ten tr words in the grid. Write them on the lines.**

t	r	a	c	t	o	r	x
t	r	o	u	s	e	r	s
t	r	i	a	n	g	l	e
t	r	u	m	p	e	t	t
t	r	i	g	g	e	r	r
x	t	r	u	n	k	a	u
t	r	a	m	p	x	y	c
t	r	u	t	r	a	c	k

_____   _____

_____   _____

_____   _____

_____   _____

_____   _____

Consonant Clusters

Name _____

1. Write these words in pairs on the lines below.
   Each pair should start with the same two letters.

swan	tractor	speak	black
blue	swallow	truck	spoke

   _____ _____ _____ _____

   _____ _____ _____ _____

2. Can you spot eight **cr** words in the box?

crowdcranecricketcrowncrustcreamcriedcrate

   Write each word beside its meaning.

   a. to have wept _____

   b. a box _____

   c. a lifting machine _____

   d. the end parts of a loaf of bread
   _____

   e. a sport _____

   f. a lot of people _____

   g. the fat of milk _____

   h. what a king or queen wears
   _____

3. Complete each word.

   Use these blends.

tr	sw	sl	sn
fl	br	gl	cr

   a. ___ ___ippers

   b. ___ ___umpet

   c. ___ ___ove

   d. ___ ___ute

   e. ___ ___own

   f. ___ ___ail

   g. ___ ___ead

   h. ___ ___ing

Consonant Clusters

Name _____

1. **Add the same blend to each group of words.**

fr	dr	br	fl
pl	sp	sk	gr

a. _____izzle   b. _____ooch   c. _____og   d. _____ush
_____agon   _____eakfast   _____ost   _____ight
_____eam   _____ass   _____ont   _____ea

e. _____ease   f. _____ease   g. _____etch   h. _____ort
_____an   _____aph   _____ull   _____ell
_____enty   _____ape   _____unk   _____aghetti

2. **Complete each sentence.**

Use these words.

crumbs	frog	graph	platypus
spaghetti	scent	trolley	stallion

a. A _____ is an Australian animal.

b. The noise made by a _____ is called a croak.

c. A type of pasta is called _____.

d. The hungry birds ate the _____ of bread thrown to them.

e. A male horse is called a _____.

f. I drew a _____ of the ways children in my year come to school.

g. The lady sprayed the _____ around the room.

h. I used the _____ to put my groceries in at the supermarket.

3. **Choose the correct blend to complete each word.**

a. _____eleton (sk sc) bones of the body   e. _____arrow (sm sp) small bird

b. _____um (pr pl) fruit   f. _____une (pr pl) dried plum

c. _____eece (fl fr) wool of a sheep   g. _____eckle (fl fr) spot on the skin

d. _____utton (gr gl) greedy person   h. _____ape (gr gl) fruit of a vine

Consonant Clusters

Name _____

1. **Complete each word.**

   Use these blends.

cl	sp	tr	bl
dr	br	fr	fl

   a. _____aniel (type of dog) **e.** _____eacle (thick sweet syrup)

   b. _____arinet (musical instrument) **f.** _____ossom (flowers of a tree)

   c. _____owsy (tired) **g.** _____agile (easily broken)

   d. _____amingo (large wading bird) **h.** _____eeze (light wind)

2. **Complete each sentence.**

   Use these words.

plough	stampede	trout	fracture
flannel	gravel	placard	scorpion

   a. The x-ray showed a _____ of the bone in his arm.

   b. The frightened cattle began to _____.

   c. When he lifted the rock Ravi saw a _____ and a spider.

   d. The farmer pulled the _____ with a tractor.

   e. The _____ was spread over the surface of the road.

   f. I caught a two-kilogram _____ in the river.

   g. It was so cold she wore thick _____ underwear.

   h. The protester carried a _____ during the march.

3. **Circle the correct word.**

   a. She plays a (trough trombone) in the orchestra.

   b. The boxing match was held in a (stadium stamina).

   c. A wise old saying is a (produce proverb).

   d. One quarter is a (fraction fracture) of a whole.

   e. A type of fish is a (flounder flotilla).

   f. A snow storm is called a (blizzard blossom).

   g. A type of metal is called (bronze brooch).

   h. A fold in cloth is called a (create crease).

10

Consonant Clusters

Name _____

1. **The words in the grid end in st. Use each word to complete a sentence.**

w	f	i	s	t
e	n	e	s	t
s	p	e	s	t
t	t	e	s	t
r	u	s	t	x
c	r	u	s	t
f	r	o	s	t

   a. The cold _____ damaged the fruit on the trees.

   b. A snail is a _____ in the garden.

   c. The bird built its _____ in the tall tree.

   d. Our teacher gave us a spelling _____.

   e. William hit the boy with his _____.

   f. I threw the small _____ to the starving birds.

   g. After travelling north we turned _____.

   h. Iron will _____ if it gets wet.

2. **Complete each sentence.**

   Use these **nt** words.

blunt	bent	grunt	plant
tent	spent	count	rent

   a. When we went camping we slept in a _____.

   b. That knife is sharp but this one is _____.

   c. Can you _____ up to fifty?

   d. A large _____ was growing in our garden.

   e. That wire is straight but this one is _____.

   f. The noise of a pig is called a _____.

   g. When we lived in the apartment we had to pay _____ each week.

   h. Mo has _____ all his money.

3. **Can you find ten words in the box? Write them below the final blend they contain.**

pastsofttrampgulppulpdriftlastmeltjoltpump

   lt   lp   ft   mp   st

   _____   _____   _____   _____   _____

   _____   _____   _____   _____   _____

Consonant Clusters

Name _____

1. **Find words in the grid. Write them below the final blend they contain.**

w	a	d	u	l	t	c
e	f	l	a	s	k	r
p	f	a	u	l	t	e
t	b	r	i	s	k	p
t	h	u	m	p	x	t
s	p	r	i	n	t	x
s	t	a	m	p	n	t
s	p	l	i	n	t	z

nt
_____
_____

pt
_____
_____

lt
_____
_____

sk
_____

mp
_____
_____

2. **Complete each word.**

Use these blends.

st	nt	mp	nd	ct	sk

a. ma_____ (face covering)

b. lea_____ (opposite of most)

c. dismou_____ (to get down from a horse)

d. po_____ (pool of water)

e. subtra_____ (opposite of add)

f. sta_____ (used to send a letter)

g. plu_____ (fat)

h. spri_____ (short race)

i. mi_____ (fog)

j. contra_____ (to get smaller)

3. **Rearrange the letters to make words that end with blends. The first one has been done for you**

a. slit (group of items) **list**

b. stud (small pieces of dirt) _____

c. cats (throw out a fishing line) _____

d. vats (huge, large) _____

e. salt (opposite of first) _____

f. stop (used to make a fence) _____

g. step (nuisance) _____

h. felt (opposite of right) _____

i. plug (drink copiously) _____

j. palm (a kind of light) _____

Consonant Clusters

Name _____

1. *What does it mean?*

vault	cataract	correct	expand
quilt	wept	stump	pretend

Which word means

a. a waterfall? _____

b. a bed covering? _____

c. sobbed? _____

d. remains of a tree when it is cut down? _____

e. opposite of wrong? _____

f. to become larger? _____

g. a safe in a bank? _____

h. to make out you are someone or something else? _____

2. Add a vowel to complete each word.

a. hmp (a camel has one) _____

b. swft (fast) _____

c. tsks (an elephant has two) _____

d. clt (young male horse) _____

e. mnd (repair) _____

f. dsk (evening) _____

g. strct (severe) _____

h. klp (seaweed) _____

3. Find words in the grid. Write them under their final blends.

e	x	c	e	p	t	a
b	t	h	u	m	p	t
r	f	a	c	t	h	t
a	l	i	m	p	e	r
n	w	i	n	d	l	a
d	w	e	p	t	p	c
y	e	l	p	x	x	t
i	n	s	u	l	t	x
r	e	s	u	l	t	x

lt

_____

_____

mp

_____

_____

ct

_____

_____

lp

_____

_____

nd

_____

_____

pt

_____

_____

Answers to Consonant Clusters

Answers to page 7

1 spade, sparrow, sport, spine, splinter, spring, spider, sponge

2 skipping, screw, prison, fruit, glasses, cloak, fleece, crane

3 tractor, trousers, triangle, trumpet, trigger, trunk, tramp, track, tray, truck

Answers to page 8

1 swan, swallow; tractor, truck; speak, spoke; black, blue

2 cried, crate, crane, crust, cricket, crowd, cream, crown

3 slippers, trumpet, glove, flute, crown, snail, bread, swing

Answers to page 9

1 drizzle, dragon, dream;
brooch, breakfast, brass;
frog, frost, front;
flush, flight, flea;
please, plan, plenty;

grease, graph, grape;
sketch, skull, skunk;
sport, spell, spaghetti

2 platypus, frog, spaghetti, crumbs, stallion, graph, scent, trolley

3 skeleton, plum, fleece, glutton, sparrow, prune, freckle, grape

Answers to page 10

1 spaniel, clarinet, drowsy, flamingo, treacle, blossom, fragile, breeze

2 fracture, stampede, scorpion, plough, gravel, trout, flannel, placard

3 trombone, stadium, proverb, fraction, flounder, blizzard, bronze, crease

Answers to page 11

1 frost, pest, nest, test, fist, crust, west, rust

2 tent, blunt, count, plant, bent, grunt, rent, spent

3 melt, jolt;
gulp, pulp;
soft, drift;
tramp, pump;
past, last

Answers to page 12

1 sprint, splint, flask, brisk, wept, crept, adult, fault, hump, stamp

2 mask, least, dismount, pond, subtract, stamp, plump, sprint, mist, contract

3 list, dust, cast, vast, last, post, pest, left, gulp, lamp

Answers to page 13

1 cataract, quilt, wept, stump, correct, expand, vault, pretend

2 hump, swift, tusk, colt, mend, dusk, strict, kelp

3 insult, result, hump, limp, fact, attract, yelp, help, wind, brand, except, wept

Introduction and Answers to Double Consonants

In Year 4 Term 1, the National Literacy Strategy introduced the letter pattern of 'two-syllable words containing double consonants, e.g. bubble, kettle, common'.

It is worth teaching the spelling rule that double consonants usually come after short vowels and single consonants after long vowels, e.g. gabble and gable, riffle and rifle, comma and coma.

It is also worth noting that after nn, rr, ss the ending –el is more common than –le, e.g. funnel, kennel, tunnel, barrel, mussel, tassel, vessel.

Answers to page 16

1 tennis, compass, bottom, Joanna, nugget, collide, swollen, follow

2 kitten, rabbit, mutton, summer, funny, button, yellow, connect, drizzle, gorilla

3 soccer, pullet, dinner, marry, hollow, dresser, village, rubber

Answers to page 17

1 lettuce, bullet, swallow, mirror, cattle, saddle, filled, battle

2 nugget, carriage, tennis, barrel, apple, pullet, bullet, cattle, current, traffic

3 cherry, traffic, pillow, saddle, swallow, terror, rudder, giraffe

Answers to page 18

1 soccer, gorilla, currant, terror, gallop, bottom, mirror, willow, porridge, cottage

2 pullet, chaff, arrest, bullet, battle, offend, current, funnel

3 gazelle, mutton, cattle, squirrel, lettuce, innocent, allowed, barrel

Answers to page 19

1 bullet, filled, pulled, tennis, dinner or digger, lolly, killed, hugged, tugged, tunnel, funnel, kennel

2 asleep, unless, passenger, discover, missed, almost, address, prison, compass, tossed, happiness, across, disappear, vessel, dissolve

3 hammock, umbrella, mutton, committee, irrigate, immune, jewellery, innocent

Double Consonants

Name _____

1. Choose the correct word to complete each sentence.

Joanna	follow	bottom	collide
compass	nugget	swollen	tennis

a. We played a game of _____ on the grass courts.

b. We used the _____ to show us what direction we were travelling in.

c. Matthew ran from the _____ to the top of the hill.

d. _____ is a girl's name.

e. The miner hid the large _____ of gold from his friends.

f. The two planes were lucky not to _____ in mid-air.

g. Because of the constant rain the rivers became _____ with water.

h. Shaheen is going to go first, then I am going to _____ her.

2. Add a set of double letters to complete each word.

a. ki____en (young cat)

b. ra____it (furry animal)

c. mu____on (meat of a sheep)

d. su____er (hot season of the year)

e. fu____y (amusing)

f. bu____on (found on a shirt)

g. ye____ow (colour)

h. co____ect (join)

i. dri____le (light rain)

j. gori____a (large ape)

3. Can you spot eight words with double consonants? Write each word beside its definition.

pulletdresserrubberhollowsoccerdinnermarryvillage

a. sport _____

b. young fowl _____

c. meal of the day _____

d. wed _____

e. not solid _____

f. piece of furniture _____

g. small town _____

h. eraser _____

Double Consonants

Name _____

1. Circle the correct word.

   a. A (lettuce carrot) is a leafy green vegetable.

   b. The (bullet ballet) hit the target.

   c. A (swallow willow) is a small bird.

   d. A (terror mirror) is also called a looking glass.

   e. Cows and bulls are called (battle cattle).

   f. The cowboy threw the (straddle saddle) over the horse's back.

   g. I (filled billed) the empty bucket with water.

   h. After the fierce (bottle battle) the soldiers rested.

2. Find and write all ten words. Each word contains double letters.

n	u	g	g	e	t	c	t
t	b	a	p	b	c	u	r
e	a	p	u	u	a	r	a
n	r	p	l	l	t	r	f
n	r	l	l	l	t	e	f
i	e	e	e	e	l	n	i
s	l	r	t	t	e	t	c
c	a	r	r	i	a	g	e

_____   _____

_____   _____

_____   _____

_____   _____

_____   _____

3. Complete each word.

Use these double letters.

dd	rr	ff	ll

   a. che____y (small red fruit)

   b. tra____ic (cars, trucks, bikes, etc.)

   c. pi____ow (head rest on a bed)

   d. sa____le (seat on a horse)

   e. swa____ow (small bird)

   f. te____or (deep fear)

   g. ru____er (used to guide a boat)

   h. gira____e (large animal)

Double Consonants

Name _____

1. **Write each word in the box beside its meaning.**

cottage	currant	gallop	porridge	willow
soccer	gorilla	terror	bottom	mirror

a. a sport _____

b. a large ape _____

c. a dried grape _____

d. fear _____

e. how a horse runs _____

f. opposite to top _____

g. looking glass _____

h. a type of tree _____

i. breakfast cereal _____

j. small house _____

2. **Draw a ring around the correct word to complete each sentence.**

a. A (pullet   pellet) is a young hen.

b. Horses are often fed on (chuff   chaff).

c. The police are going to (attest   arrest) the thief.

d. The (bullet   ballot) was fired from the rifle.

e. The soldier was wounded in the (bottle   battle).

f. The cheeky boy may (offend   attend) the old man.

g. The swift (current   currant) swept the swimmers downstream.

h. The smoke could be seen coming from the (funnel   tunnel) of the ship.

3. **Add tt, rr, ll or nn to complete each word.**

a. gaze_____e (deer-like animal)

b. mu_____on (meat of a sheep)

c. ca_____le (cows, bulls, etc.)

d. squi_____el (furry animal)

e. le_____uce (leafy vegetable)

f. i_____ocent (not guilty)

g. a_____owed (permitted)

h. ba_____el (large vat)

18

Double Consonants

Name _____

1. **Add nn, ll or gg to complete each word.**

   a. bu____et   e. di____er   i. tu____ed

   b. fi____ed   f. lo____y   j. tu____el

   c. pu____ed   g. ki____ed   k. fu____el

   d. te____is   h. hu____ed   l. ke____el

2. **Choose s or ss to complete each word.**

   a. a____leep   f. almo____t   k. happine____

   b. unle____   g. addre____   l. acro____

   c. pa____enger   h. pri____on   m. di____appear

   d. di____cover   i. compa____   n. ve____el

   e. mi____ed   j. to____ed   o. di____olve

3. **Complete each sentence.**

   Use these words.

irrigate	committee	immune	mutton
hammock	innocent	jewellery	umbrella

   a. I tied the _____ between the two trees.

   b. As it was raining steadily I decided to take my _____ to school.

   c. The meat of a sheep is called _____.

   d. Our junior school _____ decided to begin fundraising.

   e. As it is so dry, the farmers will begin to _____ their crops.

   f. These insects are now _____ to the effects of this insecticide.

   g. Expensive _____ was stolen during the burglary.

   h. The jury found the woman _____ of the charges against her.

Introduction to Identifying Phonemes

Vowel phonemes were taught in Year 2 of the National Literacy Strategy, but they still need to be practised throughout Key Stage 2.

It is still worth referring to the rule for 'magic e', i.e. the a–e, i–e, o–e, u–e pattern, which turns a short vowel into a long vowel sound, unless the consonant is doubled, e.g. mat, mate, matted; bit, bite, bitten; pop, pope, poppy; hug, huge, hugging.

This rule will recur when considering adding suffixes to verbs.

Identifying Phonemes

Name _____

1. **Write each word beside its meaning.**

   oo words

rooster	school	cocoon	loose
hoot	choose	smooth	brood

   a. not tight _____

   b. not rough _____

   c. a moth hatches from it _____

   d. noise of an owl _____

   e. select _____

   f. place of education _____

   g. male chicken _____

   h. clutch of chickens _____

2. **Use each word in a sentence.**

   g sounds **j** when followed by **e, i** or **y**.

ledge	bridge	dodge	gently
giraffe	badge	hedge	danger

   a. A new steel _____ was built across the river.

   b. She wore her football team's _____ on her jacket.

   c. The mother deer sensed the _____ when the tiger came near her fawn.

   d. The footballer had to _____ around his opponent.

   e. The girls were trapped on a _____ of the steep cliff.

   f. At the zoo we saw a buffalo and a _____.

   g. The father lifted the baby _____ from the cot.

   h. We have a tall privet _____ around our home.

3. **Circle the two rhyming words in each line.**

   a. past   night   pound   last

   b. four   pour   seat   chair

   c. ledge   hedge   hoot   want

   d. trace   door   loop   coop

   e. hose   nose   choose   brook

   f. feel   lied   shift   peel

   g. pork   crash   fork   sleeve

   h. rabbit   ugly   berry   cherry

Identifying Phonemes

Name _____

1. **Add er or or to complete each word.**

   a. tail___ ___ (person who makes clothes)

   b. rot___ ___ (helicopter blade)

   c. sail___ ___ (person who sails a ship)

   d. tig___ ___ (large cat)

   e. fing___ ___ (digit of the hand)

   f. silv___ ___ (precious metal)

   g. mot___ ___ (engine)

   h. timb___ ___ (wood)

2. **Write each word beside its meaning.**

   ee words

sleet	steel	meet	kneel
sleeve	fleet	reel	asleep

   a. not awake _____

   b. to rest on the knees _____

   c. encounter _____

   d. a metal _____

   e. a group of ships _____

   f. part of a shirt _____

   g. part of a fishing rod _____

   h. icy rain _____

3. **Write each word beside its meaning.**

   or words

shore	north	porch	stork
story	cord	forty	scorch

   a. a tale _____

   b. thick string _____

   c. a number _____

   d. to burn _____

   e. a large bird _____

   f. part of a house _____

   g. a direction _____

   h. edge of the ocean _____

Identifying Phonemes

Name _____

1. **Each word contains the ey sound. Use each to complete a sentence.**

kidney	hockey	trolley	alley	turkey
chimney	jockey	journey	honey	storey

a. The third _____ of the building was damaged in the fire.

b. I play _____ each Saturday morning.

c. We walked quickly through the _____ between the tall buildings.

d. I used a _____ to put my groceries in at the supermarket.

e. The story tells us of Marco Polo's _____ to China.

f. We had a steak and _____ pie for tea last night.

g. The tall thin _____ carried the smoke high into the sky.

h. The goose and the _____ were kept in the fowl house.

i. The _____ whipped the horse to urge it to go faster.

j. The bear robbed the hive of its _____.

2. **Find the ee words in the grid. Match them to their meanings.**

g	e	e	s	e	s	c	a
t	q	b	c	s	t	a	s
o	u	r	o	n	e	n	l
f	e	e	f	e	e	t	e
f	e	e	f	e	p	e	e
e	r	z	e	z	l	e	p
e	x	e	e	e	e	n	x

a. not awake _____

b. light wind _____

c. popular beverage _____

d. large farm birds _____

e. to push air through the nose _____

f. sticky sweet _____

g. high part of a church _____

h. strange, odd _____

i. eating place _____

3. **These words contain y. Write each beside its meaning.**

pansy	empty	platypus	library	angry
jetty	oxygen	poultry	lorry	rapidly

a. a flower _____

b. place where ships are moored _____

c. a gas _____

d. fowls, ducks, etc. _____

e. large truck _____

f. place of books _____

g. quickly _____

h. upset _____

i. Australian creature _____

j. vacant, not full _____

Identifying Phonemes

Name _____

1. **Each word in the box contains a + e. Use each to complete a sentence.**

escape	graceful	crane	paste
safety	behave	stake	chase

   a. The dog began to _____ the frightened cat.

   b. We watched the _____ movements of the ballet dancers.

   c. The prisoner tried to _____ from the small cell.

   d. When the lightning flashed we ran to the _____ of the building.

   e. Katy, who had been naughty, promised to _____ in future.

   f. The powerful _____ lifted the equipment onto the roof of the skyscraper.

   g. I hammered the wooden _____ into the ground.

   h. Mrs Smith stuck the sheets of paper together with some thick _____.

2. **Can you spot the u + e words in the box? Write each beside its meaning.**

injuremanurerescuebugleavenuefurniturefortunepuncture

   a. musical instrument _____   **e.** tables, chairs, beds, etc. _____

   b. fertiliser _____   **f.** wealth _____

   c. save _____   **g.** flat tyre _____

   d. tree-lined street _____   **h.** harm, hurt _____

3. Each of these **i + e** words can be linked to a word below. **Write each beside its link word.**

vine	hostile	mobile	dislike
entire	umpire	missile	polite

   a. angry _____   **e.** hate _____

   b. rocket _____   **f.** grape _____

   c. movable _____   **g.** rude _____

   d. whole _____   **h.** referee _____

Identifying Phonemes

Name _____

1. **Can you spot words in the grid that contain *ea*? Write each beside its meaning.**

d	s	t	e	a	k	d
e	d	l	b	r	b	r
a	e	e	r	e	r	e
f	a	a	e	a	e	a
x	d	d	a	d	a	d
a	z	x	k	y	d	x

a. not alive _____

b. heavy metal _____

c. prepared _____

d. unable to hear _____

e. cut of beef _____

f. to fear _____

g. food made from flour _____

h. to snap apart _____

2. **Add *ea*, *ai* or *aw* to complete each word.**

a. f_____n (young deer)

b. d_____sy (flower)

c. f_____st (large meal)

d. _____gle (large bird of prey)

e. w_____st (middle of your body)

f. _____ful (terrible, horrible)

g. l_____n (cut grass)

h. d_____ly (every day)

3. **Each word contains *ow*. Use each to complete a sentence.**

rainbow	arrow	hollow	sowing
elbow	burrow	sparrow	shallow

a. That pipe is solid but this one is _____.

b. The rabbit ran into its _____ to escape the dog.

c. This part of the pool is deep, but further on it is _____.

d. The farmer is _____ wheat in the fields.

e. The archer fired the _____ at the target.

f. The _____ built its nest in the tall tree.

g. She hurt her _____ when her arm hit the table.

h. It is said there is a pot of gold at the end of a _____.

Identifying Phonemes

Name _____

1. **Add oo, or ee to complete each word.**

   a. cuck_____ (bird)

   b. toff_____ (sticky sweet)

   c. qu_____r (strange, odd)

   d. st_____ple (part of a church)

   e. kangar_____ (hopping marsupial)

   f. g_____se (farmyard birds)

   g. sch_____ner (large sailing ship)

   h. coff_____ (beverage)

2. **The words in the grid contain th. Write each beside its meaning.**

t	h	i	n	k	s	x
f	e	a	t	h	e	r
t	t	c	t	w	m	o
h	h	l	h	o	o	t
u	i	o	i	r	t	h
m	e	t	g	t	h	x
b	f	h	h	h	x	r

   a. digit of the hand _____

   b. person who steals _____

   c. material _____

   d. consider _____

   e. insect _____

   f. covering of a bird _____

   g. value _____

   h. part of your leg _____

3. **Look at these words. Each contains ck.**

paddock	locket	cockatoo	wicked
buckle	wicket	chuckle	stocking

   Which word means:

   a. giggle? _____

   b. a field? _____

   c. something you need to play cricket? _____

   d. a large parrot? _____

   e. evil? _____

   f. something you wear on your legs? _____

   g. something found on a belt? _____

   h. something you wear around your neck? _____

Identifying Phonemes

Name _____

1. *What does it mean?* **Match each word to its meaning.**

   In these words, **a** has a short **o** sound.

wallet	swallow	swan	swamp	wand
quarrel	squash	wallaby	quarry	quantity

   a. small bird _____

   b. argument, disagreement _____

   c. leather container for money _____

   d. a sport _____

   e. animal like a kangaroo _____

   f. wetlands _____

   g. amount of something _____

   h. place where stone is mined _____

   i. large graceful water bird _____

   j. a magic stick _____

2. **In these words the g has a j sound. Use each in a sentence.**

cabbage	fragile	stranger	average
pigeon	engine	lounge	genius

   a. He is so clever some believe he is a _____.

   b. Our television set is in the _____ .

   c. The mechanic filled the _____ with oil.

   d. The _____ built its nest in the tall tree.

   e. The _____ age of the children is twelve.

   f. I told the teacher there was a _____ in the schoolyard.

   g. Be careful not to drop that glass as it is _____.

   h. We made some coleslaw with the _____.

3. **Each ei word can be linked to a word below. Match up the words.**

neigh	sleigh	reign	vein
eighty	freight	weight	neighbour

   a. number _____

   b. blood _____

   c. horse _____

   d. snow _____

   e. queen _____

   f. truck _____

   g. kilogram _____

   h. next door _____

Identifying Phonemes

Name _____

1. **Each of these words contains ar. Match each to its meaning.**

leopard	burglar	collar	cellar	harp
barge	lizard	orchard	circular	marble

a. flat-bottomed boat _____

b. a reptile _____

c. part of a coat or shirt _____

d. an underground room _____

e. a stringed musical instrument _____

f. a large spotted cat _____

g. a thief _____

h. round _____

i. a hard rock _____

j. a farm for fruit trees _____

2. **Each of these words contains au as in cause. Use each to complete a sentence.**

sauce	author	autumn	daughter	laundry
audience	saucer	automobile	haunt	autograph

a. The famous film star gave me her _____.

b. In _____ the leaves fall from the trees.

c. I like to have tomato _____ on my hot dog.

d. This _____ has four new tyres.

e. It is said a ghost may _____ this old house.

f. Jan is the _____ of Mr and Mrs Smith.

g. This is the third novel written by this _____.

h. The _____ clapped loudly at his wonderful act.

i. I gave a _____ of milk to my cat.

j. We washed the dirty clothes at the _____.

3. **Each of these words contains oo. Match each to its meaning.**

cuckoo	igloo	cockatoo	schooner
bamboo	moose	cartoon	kangaroo	gloomy

a. a type of large grass _____

b. a large animal of North America _____

c. a type of parrot _____

d. a bird that lays its eggs in the nest of another _____

e. a type of sailing ship _____

f. a hopping animal _____

g. dull, dreary _____

h. a home made of ice _____

i. a film made from drawings _____

Answers to Identifying Phonemes

Answers to page 21

1 loose, smooth, cocoon, hoot, choose, school, rooster, brood

2 bridge, badge, danger, dodge, ledge, giraffe, gently, hedge

3 past, last; four, pour; ledge, hedge; loop, coop; hose, nose; feel, peel; pork, fork; berry, cherry

Answers to page 22

1 tailor, rotor, sailor, tiger, finger, silver, motor, timber

2 asleep, kneel, meet, steel, fleet, sleeve, reel, sleet

3 story, cord, forty, scorch, stork, porch, north, shore

Answers to page 23

1 storey, hockey, alley, trolley, journey, kidney, chimney, turkey, jockey, honey

2 asleep, breeze, coffee, geese, sneeze, toffee, steeple, queer, canteen

3 pansy, jetty, oxygen, poultry, lorry, library, rapidly, angry, platypus, empty

Answers to page 24

1 chase, graceful, escape, safety, behave, crane, stake, paste

2 bugle, manure, rescue, avenue, furniture, fortune, puncture, injure

3 hostile, missile, mobile, entire, dislike, vine, polite, umpire

Answers to page 25

1 dead, lead, ready, deaf, steak, dread, bread, break

2 fawn, daisy, feast, eagle, waist, awful, lawn, daily

3 hollow, burrow, shallow, sowing, arrow, sparrow, elbow, rainbow

Answers to page 26

1 cuckoo, toffee, queer, steeple, kangaroo, geese, schooner, coffee

2 thumb, thief, cloth, think, moth, feather, worth, thigh

3 chuckle, paddock, wicket, cockatoo, wicked, stocking, buckle, locket

Answers to page 27

1 swallow, quarrel, wallet, squash, wallaby, swamp, quantity, quarry, swan, wand

2 genius, lounge, engine, pigeon, average, stranger, fragile, cabbage

3 eighty, vein, neigh, sleigh, reign, freight, weight, neighbour

Answers to page 28

1 barge, lizard, collar, cellar, harp, leopard, burglar, circular, marble, orchard

2 autograph, autumn, sauce, automobile, haunt, daughter, author, audience, saucer, laundry

3 bamboo, moose, cockatoo, cuckoo, schooner, kangaroo, gloomy, igloo, cartoon

Introduction to Common Letter Strings

The National Literacy Strategy specifies a very useful principle:

Y5T2 W5: to investigate words which have common letter strings but different pronunciations, e.g. rough, cough, bough; boot, foot.

This principle is crucial to English spelling: that there are common patterns of word spelling, but they do not necessarily have a direct correspondence with the sound of those letters, as in the two examples quoted above, and unlike other more regularly spelt foreign languages.

The way to help children understand these complexities is for them to group and write words by spelling family, but always to sound the words so that they are aware that the same sound may be spelt in several different ways.

Common Letter Strings

Name _____

1. **Write each word under the letter string it contains. Say each word out loud.**

bough	surround	sound	cough
mound	clover	river	knives
shovel	rough	arrive	drover

ive	ove	ough	ound
_____	_____	_____	_____
_____	_____	_____	_____
_____	_____	_____	_____

2. **Look closely at each line of words. Identify and write the common letter string.**

   a. stitch hitch switch _____   f. score shore wore _____

   b. entire desire umpire _____   g. board soar hoarse _____

   c. linen pine swine _____   h. toast roast boast _____

   d. behind blind grind _____   i. scout spout sprout _____

   e. river hive arrive _____   j. thorn morning corner _____

3. **Complete the word in each sentence.**

   Use these letter strings.

itch	ide	each	aught
atch	ast	and	ard

   a. We used bl_____ to whiten the clothes.

   b. Joan is the eldest d_____er of Mrs Smith.

   c. I stuck the picture in my book with some p_____e.

   d. We cooked the meals in the k_____en.

   e. The person who captured the thief was given a rew_____.

   f. She wore some leather s_____als to school.

   g. As it began to rain we decided to go ins_____.

   h. The baker showed me the freshly cooked b_____ of bread.

Common Letter Strings

Name _____

1. *What does it mean?* Each word in the box contains the letter string **art**. Match each word to its meaning.

heart	artist	quarter	cart
artichoke	wart	depart	party

a. to leave _____

b. a type of vegetable _____

c. one fourth _____

d. a growth on the skin _____

e. an organ of the body _____

f. a celebration _____

g. a painter _____

h. horse-drawn vehicle _____

2. Complete each word.

Use these letter strings.

eat	ear	aught	ast
oast	ive	eep	ence

a. The King lived in a large c_____le.

b. The rabbit had its foot c_____ in the trap.

c. Mr Smith has a long red b_____d.

d. The farmer sowed the wh_____ after the rain had fallen.

e. A tall f_____ was built around the yard.

f. I used a straw broom to sw_____ the yard.

g. The bees returned to their h_____ before it was dark.

h. We ate thickly buttered t_____ for breakfast.

3. Study these cramped words carefully. Underline those that contain the **use** letter string and circle those that contain the (ute) letter string.

saluteexcuserefusebruteabusedisputeparachute

museumamusecutemuteflutefuseconfuseaccusecompute

Common Letter Strings

Name _____

1. **Study the words in the box. Write them in pairs that contain the same letter string.**

drawn	attack	plant	ambush	quack
lamb	hatch	watch	slant	pawn

_____   _____   _____   _____   _____

_____   _____   _____   _____   _____

2. **Write the letter string that is common to each group of words.**

a. wart start apart _____

b. grass brass mass _____

c. bath path wrath_____

d. drawn lawn sawn _____

e. laughter taught caught _____

f. steal seal wealth _____

g. weary pear earth _____

h. please tease release _____

i. teacher bleach reach _____

j. treat theatre wheat _____

3. **Add one letter string to each group of words.**

Use these letter strings.

oar	ive	eep	ent

d_____	pres_____	f_____	cupb_____d
sh_____	b_____	r_____r	b_____d
k_____	rec_____	g_____	r_____
sw_____	pl_____y	al_____	ab_____d

Common Letter Strings

Name _____

1. **Circle the word that does not contain the same letter string.**

   a. bracket quack snack (shaft)

   b. tractor teacher reaches peaches

   c. stake chair mistake waken

   d. voyage damage sausage refrain

   e. frame wallet allow wallaby

   f. camel shame blame daily

   g. stranger orange angel garden

   h. regard reward larder stamp

   i. sample square prepare careless

   j. castle latch taste plaster

2. **The following words all contain ation. Write each beside its meaning.**

vocation	vacation	plantation	population
stationery	examination	destination	stationary

   a. letters, envelopes, etc. _____

   b. holiday _____

   c. number of people in a country _____

   d. test _____

   e. goal in a journey _____

   f. still, not moving _____

   g. occupation, goal in life _____

   h. group of trees _____

3. **Add ear, eal or eak to complete each word.**

   a. w_____y (tired)

   b. squ _____ (noise of a mouse)

   c. p_____ (sound of a bell)

   d. st_____ (take without permission)

   e. h_____t (organ of the body)

   f. b_____er (glass container)

   g. st_____ (type of meat)

   h. j_____ous (envious)

   i. _____ly (not late)

   j. w_____ (not strong)

Common Letter Strings

Name _____

1. **Add the same letter string to the words in each group.**

ease	eer	each	eath

a. p_____ (a fruit)

    bl_____ (whitener)

    b_____ (seaside)

b. l_____er (hide of animals)

    f_____er (covering of birds)

    w_____er (climate)

c. qu_____ (strange, odd)

    b_____ (alcoholic drink)

    car_____ (occupation)

d. gr_____ (lubricant)

    dis_____ (illness)

    t_____ (torment)

2. **Add a word from the box that contains the same letter pattern.**

inside	round	spice	morning	invisible
tough	never	sign	donkey	relief

a. turkey monkey _____

b. gnash gnome _____

c. sever lever _____

d. chief brief _____

e. practice advice _____

f. tide wide _____

g. impossible terrible _____

h. astound sound _____

i. bough rough _____

j. corner sworn _____

3. **Search through each row of words. Circle the (ove) words and underline the ose words.**

droverwhosethosecloverroseremoveglovleclosethose

coversupposeshovelhovelnoseposeovershovelose

Common Letter Strings

Name _____

1. **In the grid find all the words that contain the following patterns: oar out orn.**
   Use each to complete a sentence.

t	a	c	o	r	n
r	b	r	o	a	r
o	o	h	o	r	n
u	a	s	o	a	r
t	r	t	o	r	n
c	o	r	n	e	r
r	o	u	t	e	x
h	o	a	r	s	e

a. Our house is on the _____ of the two streets.

b. A male pig is called a _____.

c. We watched the kite _____ in the air.

d. The sound of a lion is called a _____.

e. He has talked so much his voice is _____.

f. The motorist tooted her _____.

g. The fruit of an oak tree is called an _____.

h. A _____ is a freshwater fish.

i. His shirt was _____ by the prickles.

2. **Write these words in pairs that contain the same letter string.**

toast	decrease	wealth	bleach	heal
teacher	drawn	spawn	please	roast

_____ _____ _____ _____ _____

_____ _____ _____ _____ _____

3. **Add one letter string to each group of words.**

Use these letter strings.

een	dge	ease	eer

ch_____	dis_____	ba_____	qu_____
pion_____	pl_____	he_____	gr_____
st_____	incr_____	le_____	s_____
b_____	t_____	porri_____	betw_____

Common Letter Strings

Name _____

1. Find words in the grid. Write them under the letter pattern they contain.

m	w	a	l	l	e	t	c
i	c	a	s	t	l	e	o
s	d	e	c	i	d	e	v
t	c	o	r	n	e	r	e
a	s	h	o	v	e	l	r
k	a	c	o	r	n	w	c
e	a	l	l	o	w	i	a
t	a	s	t	e	x	d	k
b	r	i	d	e	x	e	e

ake _____   all _____

_____   _____

ast _____   ide _____

_____   _____

orn _____   ove _____

_____   _____

2. Complete each word.

Use these.

amp	and	air	all	age
eat	ear	ant	atch	art

a. rep_____ (to fix or mend)

b. w _____ (timepiece)

c. he_____ (body organ)

d. s_____als (footwear)

e. sw_____ (wetland)

f. w_____y (tired)

g. th_____re (place to watch plays)

h. w_____aby (hopping animal)

i. inf_____ (child)

j. saus_____ (meat in skins)

3. Write the pattern common to each group.

a. bread bead ready _____

b. brief grief relief _____

c. knight delight mighty _____

d. rough cough though _____

e. roast toast boast _____

f. boar coarse hoarse _____

g. expire desire wireless _____

h. swine linen wine _____

i. stitch hitch kitchen _____

j. arrest protest question _____

37

Common Letter Strings

Name _____

1. Find the **tch** words in the grid. Use them to complete each sentence.

c	a	t	c	h	k	s	s
w	h	b	w	i	i	a	c
a	a	a	i	t	t	t	r
t	t	t	t	c	c	c	a
c	c	c	c	h	h	h	t
h	h	h	h	x	e	e	c
m	a	t	c	h	n	l	h

a. The chickens should _____ soon.

b. He tried to _____ the ball.

c. She wore a gold _____ on her wrist.

d. The baker has a new _____ of bread.

e. The _____ cast a magic spell.

f. We cooked the food in the _____.

g. I carried my books in a _____.

h. I lit the fire with a _____.

i. The insect bite made my skin _____.

j. The kitten tried to _____ my hands.

2. Each of these **le** words can be linked to a word below. Write each word beside its link word.

saddle	candle	paddle	couple	needle
apple	cradle	poodle	bugle	tremble

a. baby _____

b. birthday _____

c. pair _____

d. shake _____

e. fruit _____

f. horse _____

g. canoe _____

h. dog _____

i. sew _____

j. music _____

3. Cramped **or** words. Write each beside its meaning.

tractoranchormirrorporpoiseorchardgorillaauthorscissors

a. looking glass _____

b. farm machine _____

c. where fruit trees grow _____

d. large ape _____

e. writer of books _____

f. object to moor ships _____

g. sea creature like a dolphin _____

h. cutting implements _____

Answers to Common Letter Strings

Answers to page 31

1 river, knives, arrive; clover, shovel, drover; bough, cough, rough; surround, sound, mound

2 itch, ire, ine, ind, ive, ore, oar, oast, out, orn

3 bleach, daughter, paste, kitchen, reward, sandals, inside, batch

Answers to page 32

1 depart, artichoke, quarter, wart, heart, party, artist, cart

2 castle, caught, beard, wheat, fence, sweep, hive, toast

3 **use**: excuse, refuse, abuse, museum, amuse, fuse, confuse, accuse

ute: salute, brute, dispute, parachute, cute, mute, flute, compute

Answers to page 33

1 drawn, pawn; attack, quack; plant, slant; ambush, lamb; hatch, watch

2 art, ass, ath, awn, aught, eal, ear, ease, each, eat

3 eep, ent, ive, oar

Answers to page 34

1 tractor, chair, refrain, frame, daily, garden, stamp, sample, latch

2 stationery, vacation, population, examination, destination, stationary, vocation, plantation

3 weary, squeak, peal, steal, heart, beaker, steak, jealous, early, weak

Answers to page 35

1 each, eath, eer, ease

2 donkey, sign, never, relief, spice, inside, invisible, round, tough, morning

3 **ove**: drover, clover, remove, glove, cover, shovel, hovel, over, shove

ose: whose, those, rose, close, those, suppose, nose, pose, lose

Answers to page 36

1 corner, boar, soar, roar, hoarse, horn, acorn, trout, torn

2 toast, roast; decrease, please; wealth, heal; bleach, teacher; drawn, spawn

3 eer, ease, dge, een

Answers to page 37

1 mistake, cake, take; castle, taste; corner, acorn; wallet, allow; decide, bride, wide; shovel, cover

2 repair, watch, heart, sandals, swamp, weary, theatre, wallaby, infant, sausage

3 ead, icf, ight, ough, oast, oar, ire, ine, itch, est

Answers to page 38

1 hatch, catch, watch, batch, witch, kitchen, satchel, match, itch, scratch

2 cradle, candle, couple, tremble, apple, saddle, paddle, poodle, needle, bugle

3 mirror, tractor, orchard, gorilla, author, anchor, porpoise, scissors

Introduction to Homophones

For the reasons referred to in the introduction to common letter strings, the English language abounds in homophones: words where common sounds can be spelt in a host of different ways, with totally different meanings.

The National Literacy Strategy advises that the problem of homophones be confronted head-on:

Y5T2 W6: to distinguish between homophones, i.e. words with common pronunciations but different spellings, e.g. eight, ate; grate, great; rain, rein, reign;

whereas there is a school of thought that prefers to keep homophones apart, to help embed each word and its spelling individually.

Knowledge of word origins could be one solution in tracing the derivation and hence spelling of the word; but in most cases this would not be realistic, and the better solution is to practise writing the correct word in context, as a way of building visual association with the word pattern and its meaning. We start this section with lists of homophones which children may refer to when completing the worksheets.

Homophones

Name _____

Homophones are words that sound the same but have different spellings and different meanings. It can be difficult to remember how to spell them properly. Here are some to get you started.

air — heir	allowed — aloud
band — banned	bare — bear
beach — beech	barren — baron
beat — beet	berry — bury
berth — birth	boar — bore
born — borne	boarder — border
bow — bough	bridle — bridal
brake — break	bread — bred
ceiling — sealing	caught — court
cereal — serial	coarse — course
colonel — kernel	current — currant
check — cheque	choose — chews
chord — cord	complement — compliment
council — counsel	days — daze
desert — dessert	dew — due
grown — groan	guessed — guest
hall — haul	him — hymn
horde — hoard	heal — heel
horse — hoarse	hire — higher
idle — idol	knows — nose
lain — lane	lead — led

Homophones

Name _____

lesson — lessen

main — mane

loan — lone

medal — meddle

mist — missed

metal — mettle

might — mite

patients — patience

praise — prays

rap — wrap

ring — wring

sauce — source

sight — site

tear — tier

stile — style

vain — vein

waist — waste

weather — whether

who's — whose

to — too — two

cent — scent — sent

for — fore — four

rite — write — right

saw — soar — sore

sew — so — sow

lightning — lightening

manner — manor

mare — mayor

miner — minor

muscle — mussel

morn — mourn

passed — past

pause — paws

principal — principle

right — write

root — route

slay — sleigh

seam — seem

throne — thrown

straight — strait

wail — whale

wait — weight

yoke — yolk

profit — prophet

aisle — I'll — isle

ewe — yew — you

rain — reign — rein

rode — rowed — road

seas — seize — sees

ware — where — wear

Homophones

1. **Write a homophone for each of these words.**

   Homophones are words that sound the same but are spelt differently.

   a. blew _____   f. fair _____

   b. brakes _____   g. fur _____

   c. berry _____   h. flour _____

   d. deer _____   i. wear _____

   e. sore _____   j. their _____

2. **Rearrange the letters to make a word to match the meaning.**

   a. bare (large animal) _____   e. cents (perfume) _____

   b. baker (to snap in two) _____   f. rates (to gaze at) _____

   c. near (to gain) _____   g. steal (old, not fresh) _____

   d. panel (flying machine) _____   h. disease (beach) _____

3. **Write a homophone for each of these words.**

   a. court _____   f. steal _____

   b. bare _____   g. pour _____

   c. fourth _____   h. waste _____

   d. scene _____   i. weight _____

   e. scent _____   j. witch _____

Homophones

Name _____

1. **Circle the correct word.**

   a. wail — a large mammal
      whale

   b. mist — failed to hit
      missed

   c. waist — rubbish
      waste

   d. throne — seat of a king
      thrown

   e. mare — female horse
      mayor

   f. lead — heavy metal
      led

   g. bow — part of a tree
      bough

   h. cereal — breakfast food
      serial

   i. horse — large animal
      hoarse

2. **Find words in the grid. Write each beside its homophone.**

m	i	s	t	p	m	w
y	r	h	h	a	i	h
o	a	y	a	u	g	o
l	i	m	l	s	h	s
k	n	n	l	e	t	e

   yoke _____   him _____

   reign _____   haul _____

   missed _____   paws _____

   mite _____   who's _____

3. **Find the homophone pairs. Write them on the lines.**

vain	grown	slay
strait	vane	for
chews	four	straight
sleigh	choose	groan

   _____   _____

   _____   _____

   _____   _____

   _____   _____

   _____   _____

Homophones

Name _____

1. **Circle the correct word.**

   a. The large brown (**bear** **bare**) chased the hunters.

   b. We toasted the slices of (**bred** **bread**).

   c. The money is (**due** **dew**) to be paid by next Thursday.

   d. She had a large blister on the (**heel** **heal**) of her foot.

   e. I wiped my (**nose** **knows**) with a handkerchief.

   f. Do you think you can (**beet** **beat**) her at spelling?

   g. Be careful or the glass will (**break** **brake**).

   h. There are only four shopping (**daze** **days**) before Christmas.

2. **Write each word beside its homophone.**

rode	ring	soar	loan	bore	beach
wear	write	sent	too	berry	main

   a. boar _____

   b. beech _____

   c. mane _____

   d. scent _____

   e. road _____

   f. where _____

   g. bury _____

   h. right _____

   i. lone _____

   j. wring _____

   k. sore _____

   l. two _____

3. **Complete each sentence. Use the homophones of these words.**

bridal	you	source	two
scent	wring	road	knot

   a. I put tomato _____ on my pie.

   b. The jockey put the _____ on the horse.

   c. I _____ a letter at the post office.

   d. Mum said she was _____ tired to take us swimming.

   e. A female sheep is called a _____.

   f. Shaheen _____ the horse down the track.

   g. When I looked they were _____ in the box.

   h. The teacher asked me to _____ the bell at ten o'clock.

Homophones

Choose the correct word, then complete each sentence.

1. **a.** That is _____ car in the garage. (**their** **there**)

    b. Sally is not _____ to go to the disco. (**aloud** **allowed**)

    c. The seeds were _____ away by the wind. (**borne** **born**)

    d. The dog began to _____ the bone. (**bury** **berry**)

    e. Greyhounds are dogs that are _____ for racing. (**bread** **bred**)

    f. My mother wrote a _____ for fifty pounds. (**cheque** **check**)

    g. A desert is a very _____ place. (**baron** **barren**)

    h. The female dog gave _____ to seven puppies. (**berth** **birth**)

2. **a.** Smoking is _____ in this restaurant. (**band** **banned**)

    b. We stopped at the _____ to show our passports. (**border** **boarder**)

    c. My dog _____ a rabbit yesterday. (**court** **caught**)

    d. Porridge is my favourite breakfast _____. (**cereal** **serial**)

    e. Sandpaper is usually very _____. (**coarse** **course**)

    f. Did you _____ the glass? (**brake** **break**)

    g. The _____ ordered the soldiers to advance. (**kernel** **colonel**)

    h. When is my next assignment _____? (**due** **dew**)

3. **a.** I asked her to _____ the drink she wanted. (**chews** **choose**)

    b. I had apple pie and cream for _____. (**dessert** **desert**)

    c. The next town is _____ than I thought. (**father** **farther**)

    d. A fully _____ giraffe is very tall. (**groan** **grown**)

    e. She had a blister on the _____ of her foot. (**heel** **heal**)

    f. The old engine has lain _____ for months. (**idle** **idol**)

    g. His throat was _____ from all the shouting he did. (**hoarse** **horse**)

    h. The swift _____ swept the swimmers away. (**current** **currant**)

Homophones

Name _____

1. **Choose the correct word to complete each sentence.**

   a. The _____ of our city declared a holiday. (mayor mare)

   b. A _____ fox was seen in the field. (loan lone)

   c. The _____ struck the trees. (lightning lightening)

   d. Our teacher gave us a _____ on gravity. (lesson lessen)

   e. A miser is a person who tries to _____ money. (horde hoard)

   f. The _____ in his right arm is quite painful. (mussel muscle)

   g. Our _____ is staying until Friday. (guest guessed)

2. **Choose the correct word to complete each sentence.**

   a. The college _____ comes from Cardiff. (principle principal)

   b. What _____ did you take to Scotland on your recent trip? (root route)

   c. The small boy was _____ to the ground by a bully. (throne thrown)

   d. Blood is flowing through this _____. (vain vein)

   e. I asked for some tomato _____ to put on the pie. (sauce source)

   f. Fotini _____ the ball on to Michael. (past passed)

   g. The knight tried to _____ the dragon. (sleigh slay)

3. **Find the words and then write each beside its homophone.**

w	r	o	a	d	w	s	s
e	w	a	i	t	a	i	e
a	r	a	i	n	i	t	a
r	t	e	a	r	l	e	m
m	i	t	e	k	n	o	t
m	a	n	o	r	y	o	u
s	e	n	t	i	s	l	e

tier _____   whale _____

reign _____   where _____

might _____   not _____

sight _____   weight _____

rowed _____   seem _____

ewe _____   manner _____

aisle _____   scent _____

Answers to Homophones

Answers to page 43

1 blue, breaks, bury, dear, saw, fare, fir, flower, where, there

2 bear, break, earn, plane, scent, stare, stale, seaside

3 caught, bear, forth, seen, sent, steel, poor, waist, wait, which

Answers to page 44

1 whale, missed, waste, throne, mare, lead, bough, cereal, horse

2 yolk, rain, mist, might, hymn, hall, pause, whose

3 vain, vane;
strait, straight;
chews, choose;
sleigh, slay;
grown, groan;
four, for

Answers to page 45

1 bear, bread, due, heel, nose, beat, break, days

2 bore, beach, main, sent, rode, wear, berry, write, loan, ring, soar, too

3 sauce, bridle, sent, too, ewe, rode, not, ring

Answers to page 46

1 their, allowed, borne, bury, bred, cheque, barren, birth

2 banned, border, caught, cereal, coarse, break, colonel, due

3 choose, dessert, farther, grown, heel, idle, hoarse, current

Answers to page 47

1 mayor, lone, lightning, lesson, hoard, muscle, guest

2 principal, route, thrown, vein, sauce, passed, slay

3 tear, rain, mite, site, road, you, isle, wail, wear, knot, wait, seam, manor, sent

Introduction and Answers to Synonyms and Antonyms

Synonyms and antonyms are revisited in Year 5, under Vocabulary extension:

Y5T1 W7: to explain the differences between synonyms, e.g. angry, irritated, frustrated, upset; collect, classify and order sets of words to identify shades of meaning;

Y5T2 W10: to investigate further antonyms. Investigate common spelling patterns and other ways of creating opposites through additional words and phrases.

In both cases, you will clearly want to introduce the use of thesauruses and dictionaries to help pupils extend their knowledge and interest in vocabulary.

Answers to page 50

1 enormous, tasty, moan, delighted, cross, crowded, good, tiny, bright, mumble

2 bright, won, running, poor, before, catch, died, part, bought, living

3 incomplete, illegal, dishonest, nonsense, unusual, improbable

Answers to page 51

1 giant, float, true, simple, answer, busy, empty, escape, strange, bottom

2 escape, mistake, cabin, holiday, discovered, perfect, worth, built, afraid, plenty

3 Answers may vary, but suggest: pleased, glad, happy, delighted, ecstatic

Synonyms and Antonyms

Name _____

1. *Synonyms.*   Match each word to the word with a similar meaning.

cross	good	mumble	delighted	tiny
enormous	crowded	tasty	moan	bright

a. huge _____

b. delicious _____

c. complain _____

d. happy _____

e. angry _____

f. busy _____

g. kind _____

h. small _____

i. clever _____

j. whisper_____

2. *Antonyms.*   An antonym is a word meaning the opposite to another word. Match each word to its antonym.

part	catch	bright	living	died
before	bought	won	running	poor

a. dull _____

b. lost _____

c. still _____

d. wealthy _____

e. after _____

f. drop _____

g. born _____

h. whole _____

i. sold _____

j. dead _____

3. *Antonyms.*   Some antonyms can be formed by adding a prefix to the word. For example, im + possible = impossible. Use the prefixes in the box to make antonyms for the words below.

un	im	dis	in	il	non

a. ____complete

b. ____legal

c. ____honest

d. ____sense

e. ____usual

f. ____probable

Synonyms and Antonyms

Name _____

1. *Antonyms.* **Write each word beside its opposite.**

escape	answer	bottom	busy	empty
giant	float	strange	true	simple

a. dwarf _____

b. sink _____

c. false _____

d. complex _____

e. question _____

f. idle _____

g. full _____

h. capture _____

i. normal _____

j. top _____

2. *Synonyms.* **Write each word beside the word that means the same.**

built	discovered	worth	plenty	perfect
afraid	escape	holiday	mistake	cabin

a. elude _____

b. error _____

c. hut _____

d. vacation _____

e. found _____

f. ideal _____

g. value _____

h. erected _____

i. frightened _____

j. many _____

3. *Synonyms.* **Synonyms are words with similar meanings. Some synonyms mean slightly different things and can give different shades of meaning. For example, scared is a stronger word than nervous. Sort this list of synonyms, starting with the "weakest" and ending with the "strongest".**

ecstatic	happy	pleased	delighted	glad

Introduction to Plurals

There are five established rules for making plurals, which can be extrapolated from the objective in the National Literacy Strategy:

Y5T1 W5: to investigate, collect and classify spelling patterns in pluralisation, construct rules for regular spellings, e.g.

- add –s to most words;

- add –es to most words ending in –s, –ss, –sh, –ch, –x, –zz;

- change –f or –fe to –ves;

- when –y is preceded by a consonant, change to –ies;

- when –y is preceded by a vowel, add –s.

To which one can add a few further rules:

exceptions to the –f rule: words ending in –ff, e.g. cliff; words ending in –ief, e.g. chief; words ending in –oof or –eef, e.g. roof and reef;

words ending in –o add –es, unless they are foreign in origin, e.g. pianos;

words of Latin or Greek origin follow their derived pluralisation, e.g. cactus, cacti; datum, data; criterion, criteria;

words that don't have separate singular and plural, e.g. sheep, deer, trousers, scissors;

totally irregular plurals, e.g. goose, geese; foot, feet; tooth, teeth; mouse, mice; child, children.

Plurals

Name _____

1. **Write the correct plural of each word.**

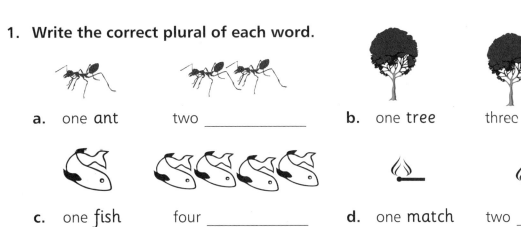

   a. one **ant**   two _____   **b.** one **tree**   three _____

   c. one **fish**   four _____   **d.** one **match**   two _____

   e. one **glass**   two _____   **f.** one **watch**   two _____

2. **Make the word in brackets mean more than one. Write it in the space.**

   a. Michelle has two blue _____. (**dress**)

   b. I ate three _____ for breakfast. (**egg**)

   c. Raj dropped the five _____. (**glass**)

   d. I sewed three _____ on my trousers. (**patch**)

   e. This tree has a lot of _____. (**branch**)

   f. There are seven _____ in the cage. (**animal**)

3. **Make the word in brackets mean more than one. Write it in the space.**

   a. I saw two _____ in the woods. (**fox**)

   b. Lots of _____ bring children to our school. (**bus**)

   c. The wizard gave me three magic _____. (**wish**)

   d. The boxer landed several _____ on his opponent. (**punch**)

   e. There are lots of _____ on top of the table. (**box**)

   f. My father has two _____ who tell him what to do. (**boss**)

53

Plurals

1. **Change the word into its plural form. Write it in the space.**

   a. one monkey   two _____   **b.** one toy   three _____

   c. one sweet   two _____   **d.** one fly   five _____

   e. one baby   two _____   **f.** one pony   two _____

2. **Make the word in brackets mean more than one. Write it in the space.**

   a. There are lots of large _____ in the world. (city)

   b. There are only three shopping _____ until Christmas. (day)

   c. Our teacher read us two _____ about snakes. (story)

   d. The _____ dismounted from their horses. (jockey)

   e. We picked all the _____ from the tree. (cherry)

   f. This supermarket has lots of _____. (trolley)

3. **Make each word mean more than one.**

   a. one loaf   two _____   **e.** one half   several _____

   b. one leaf   two _____   **f.** one elf   nine _____

   c. one shelf   three _____   **g.** one chief   three _____

   d. one cliff   two _____   **h.** one wolf   lots of _____

Plurals

Name _____

1. Change each word to mean more than one.

a. one bus   two _____   b. one gas   two _____

c. one peach   two _____   d. one church   two _____

e. one brush   two _____   f. one beach   two _____

g. one tomato   two _____   h. one leaf   two _____

2. Complete each sentence.

a. The children ate all the _____. (lolly)

b. The children ate all the _____ and left none for me. (jelly)

c. There are lots of _____ on our farm. (turkey)

d. Our city has two large _____. (library)

e. When I get to school I carry out all my _____. (duty)

f. I picked several _____ to put in the vase. (poppy)

g. We ate several _____ for tea last night. (kidney)

h. The farmer connected the two _____ to lift the loads. (pulley)

3. Make each word mean more than one.

a. one dress   two _____   e. one glass   two _____

b. one army   two _____   f. one sheep   two _____

c. one elf   two _____   g. one witch   two _____

d. one life   two _____   h. one flash   two _____

Plurals

Name _____

1. **Make the word in brackets mean more than one. Write it in the space.**

   a. There are two _____ in this tribe. (chief)

   b. We cut the oranges into _____. (half)

   c. The three _____ were arrested by the police. (thief)

   d. The baker gave me seven _____ of bread. (loaf)

   e. The men and their _____ are touring on the Costa Brava. (wife)

   f. We stacked the books on the two bottom _____. (shelf)

   g. The _____ were driven off by the noise of the guns. (wolf)

   h. We swept up all the fallen _____ in the garden. (leaf)

2. **Make the word in brackets mean more than one. Write it in the space.**

   a. I peeled all the _____ and put them in the pan. (potato)

   b. We have two _____ at home. (piano)

   c. We watched in awe as the two _____ erupted. (volcano)

   d. There were three _____ in the enclosure. (kangaroo)

   e. I cut up all the _____ and put them in the salad. (tomato)

   f. The _____ who rescued the children were awarded medals. (hero)

   g. We took lots of _____ at the wedding. (photo)

   h. All the frightened _____ stampeded across the plain. (buffalo)

3. **Make the word in brackets mean more than one. Write it in the space.**

   a. We watched as the three _____ dived into the pool. (child)

   b. There are thousands of _____ destroying the grain. (mouse)

   c. The dentist extracted four of my _____. (tooth)

   d. The flock of _____ hissed at the cat. (goose)

   e. Both of Michael's _____ are very sore. (foot)

   f. We found several _____ in the dog's basket. (louse)

   g. There were several _____ in the room. (woman)

   h. The eight _____ dragged the logs to the mill. (ox)

Plurals

Change these nouns from singular to plural.

car	**cars**	wave	_____	shop	_____
match	_____	rat	_____	punch	_____
wing	_____	patch	_____	boat	_____
watch	_____	egg	_____	branch	_____
pencil	_____	witch	_____	animal	_____

brush	_____	fox	_____	hiss	_____
gas	_____	boss	_____	dress	_____
bus	_____	kiss	_____	loss	_____
box	_____	flash	_____	glass	_____
guess	_____	wish	_____	ass	_____

monkey	_____	poppy	_____	pulley	_____
city	_____	sky	_____	kidney	_____
army	_____	story	_____	turkey	_____
fly	_____	body	_____	jockey	_____
duty	_____	jelly	_____	library	_____

roof	_____	wolf	_____	leaf	_____
reef	_____	calf	_____	elf	_____
half	_____	shelf	_____	wife	_____
loaf	_____	chief	_____	sheaf	_____
thief	_____	cliff	_____	life	_____

potato	_____	hero	_____	bamboo	_____
tomato	_____	radio	_____	boo	_____
piano	_____	kangaroo	_____	banjo	_____
buffalo	_____	mango	_____	shampoo	_____

From Time-Savers for Teachers: Spelling Years 5-6. This page may be reproduced for classroom use.

57

Answers to Plurals

Answers to page 53

1 ants, trees, fish or fishes, matches, glasses, watches

2 dresses, eggs, glasses, patches, branches, animals

3 foxes, buses, wishes, punches, boxes, bosses

Answers to page 54

1 monkeys, toys, sweets, flies, babies, ponies

2 cities, days, stories, jockeys, cherries, trolleys

3 loaves, leaves, shelves, cliffs, halves, elves, chiefs, wolves

Answers to page 55

1 buses, gases, peaches, churches, brushes, beaches, tomatoes, leaves

2 lollies, jellies, turkeys, libraries, duties, poppies, kidneys, pulleys

3 dresses, armies, elves, lives, glasses, sheep, witches, flashes

Answers to page 56

1 chiefs, halves, thieves, loaves, wives, shelves, wolves, leaves

2 potatoes, pianos, volcanoes, kangaroos, tomatoes, heroes, photos, buffaloes

3 children, mice, teeth, geese, feet, lice, women, oxen

Answers to page 57

matches, wings, watches, pencils, waves, rats, patches, eggs, witches, shops, punches, boats, branches, animals

brushes, gases, buses, boxes, guesses, foxes, bosses, kisses, flashes, wishes, hisses, dresses, losses, glasses, asses

monkeys, cities, armies, flies, duties, poppies, skies, stories, bodies, jellies, pulleys, kidneys, turkeys, jockeys, libraries

roofs, reefs, halves, loaves, thieves, wolves, calves, shelves, chiefs, cliffs, leaves, elves, wives, sheaves, lives

potatoes, tomatoes, pianos, buffaloes, heroes, radios, kangaroos, mangoes, bamboos, boos, banjoes or banjos, shampoos

Introduction and Answers to Contractions

Learning to spell contractions is essentially a question of grammatical understanding, but the National Literacy Strategy also makes a reference under Word level work:

Y4T3 W10: to distinguish the two forms: its (possessive no apostrophe) and it's (contracted 'it is') and to use these accurately in own writing.

It can help to work in both directions, from the full spelling to the contraction, and also from the contraction to the full grammatical form.

Answers to page 61

1 We have, You will, It is, did not, You are, They will

2 we are, do not, had not, I will, we have, he will, what is, I have, we are, there is, you had or you would

3 They're, What's, She's, There's, You'd

Answers to page 62

1 she had or she would, had not, they have, you have, what is, you had or you would, was not, we will, they are

2 She'd, They'll, we're, she's, we'd, they're, they'd, you'd

3 shouldn't, haven't; he'll, we'll; you've, we've; you're, they're; they'd, I'd

Contractions

Name _____

Contractions are formed when one or more letters are omitted from a word and replaced with an apostrophe.

Contractions with **is**

that's — that is   there's — there is   what's — what is
where's — where is   she's — she is   he's — he is
it's — it is

Contractions with **are**

you're — you are   they're — they are   we're — we are

Contractions with **not**

hadn't — had not   haven't — have not   shouldn't — should not
weren't — were not   wouldn't — would not   didn't — did not
don't — do not   wasn't — was not

Contractions with **will**

he'll — he will   we'll — we will   you'll — you will
they'll — they will   I'll — I will

Contractions with **have**

you've — you have   we've — we have   they've — they have
I've — I have

Contractions with **had** or **would**

he'd — he had (would)   you'd — you had (would)   she'd — she had (would)
they'd — they had (would) I'd — I had (would)   we'd — we had (would)

Contractions

Name _____

1. **Rewrite each sentence. Replace the contraction with the two words it is formed from. The first one has been done for you.**

    "What's the time?" asked Asha.

    "**What is** the time?" asked Asha.

   a. "We've only ten lollies left in the jar," said Joe.

   _____

   b. "You'll have to be lucky," shouted Nguyen.

   _____

   c. It's often hot at this time of the year.

   _____

   d. "Maurice **didn't** do it," protested Margaret.

   _____

   e. "You're not being very fair," yelled Laura.

   _____

   f. "They'll have to hurry to be ready in time," growled Mr Smith.

   _____

2. **Write the two words that make up each of these contractions.**

   a. we're _____ _____   e. we've _____ _____   i. we're _____ _____
   b. don't _____ _____   f. he'll _____ _____   j. there's _____ _____
   c. hadn't _____ _____   g. what's _____ _____   k. you'd _____ _____
   d. I'll _____ _____   h. I've _____ _____

3. **Rewrite the sentence using a contraction.**

   a. "They are not coming with us," said Sun Yen.

   _____

   b. "What is the time?" asked David.

   _____

   c. "She is the only one left in the contest," said Robyn.

   _____

   d. "There is only one apple left," moaned Joanne.

   _____

   e. "You would be warmer with a thick coat," said Ainslie.

   _____

Contractions

1. **Write the two words that make up each contraction.**

    a. she'd _____ _____   **b.** hadn't _____ _____   **c.** they've _____ _____

    d. you've _____ _____   **e.** what's _____ _____   **f.** you'd _____ _____

    g. wasn't _____ _____   **h.** we'll _____ _____   **i.** they're _____ _____

2. **Rewrite the sentence using a contraction.**

    a. **She would** have won if she hadn't tripped over.

    _____

    b. **They will** have to hurry or they will be late.

    _____

    c. We don't know where **we are** going.

    _____

    d. They told me that **she is** the best runner in the school.

    _____

    e. We didn't go because **we had** left too late.

    _____

    f. The teacher said **they are** not allowed to come.

    _____

    g. We found **they had** not even left yet.

    _____

    h. They told me **you would** get the prize later.

    _____

3. **Look at the contractions. Write each under the word it contains.**
    e.g. didn't = not

they'd	he'll	haven't	you've	you're
they're	shouldn't	I'd	we've	we'll

    not   will   have   are   would

    _____   _____   _____   _____   _____

    _____   _____   _____   _____   _____

Introduction to Prefixes and Suffixes

The National Literacy Strategy builds on the principle of identifying word roots, to which may be added prefixes or suffixes. It also emphasises the spelling rules when adding suffixes:

Y5T1 W8: to identify word roots, derivations and spelling patterns, e.g. sign, signature, signal; bomb, bombastic, bombard; remit, permit, permission, in order to extend vocabulary and provide support for spelling;

Y5T2 W4: to explore spelling patterns of consonants and formulate rules:

- –ll in full becomes l when used as a suffix;

- words ending with a single consonant preceded by a short vowel double the consonant before adding –ing, etc. e.g. hummed, sitting, wetter;

Y5T3 W5: to investigate and learn spelling rules:

- words ending in modifying e, drop e when adding ing, e.g. taking;

- words ending in modifying e, keep e when adding a suffix beginning with a consonant, e.g. hopeful, lovely;

- words ending in y preceded by a consonant change y to ie when adding a suffix, e.g. flies, tried – except for the suffixes ly or ing, e.g. shyly, flying;

- i before e except after c when the sound is ee, e.g. receive. Note and learn exceptions;

Y5T3 W7: to recognise the spelling and meaning of the prefixes: in–, im–, ir–, il–, pro–, sus–.

Prefixes and Suffixes

Name _____

1. Write the base word for each of the following.
   The first one has been done for you.

   a. dining   = **dine**   f. racing   = _____

   b. changing = _____   g. shaking = _____

   c. waving   = _____   h. shining = _____

   d. icing   = _____   i. loving   = _____

   e. tasting = _____   j. riding   = _____

2. Write the base word. The first one has been done for you.

   a. dragged = **drag**   f. mapping = _____

   b. hummed   = _____   g. stepping = _____

   c. chopped = _____   h. skinning = _____

   d. clapped = _____   i. shopping = _____

   e. skipped = _____   j. robbing = _____

3. Add the base word and suffix to make a new word.

   a. shy + ly   = **shyly**   f. sad + ness   = _____

   b. treat + ment = _____   g. slow + er   = _____

   c. fool + ish   = _____   h. grace + ful = _____

   d. help + less = _____   i. long + est   = _____

   e. hope + ful   = _____   j. sick + ness = _____

64

Prefixes and Suffixes

Name _____

1. *Opposites.* **Add a prefix to make each of these words mean the opposite.**

| dis | im | un |

   a. Ruby is very _____ happy since she lost her kitten.

   b. It is _____ possible for people to fly by flapping their arms.

   c. The spoilt child continued to _____ obey her teacher.

   d. His behaviour was _____ appointing.

   e. The decision the umpire made was _____ fair.

   f. We watched the plane _____ appear into the clouds.

   g. It is very _____ polite to snatch things from others.

   h. When we arrived we began to _____ pack our suitcases.

2. **The prefix ex means out. Match each word with its meaning.**

   a. dear, costly   example

   b. a display, public show   excavate

   c. a journey for a special purpose   experiment

   d. a test to discover something new   exhibition

   e. to dig   expensive

   f. a model of something   excursion

3. **Add a prefix to complete each word so that the sentences make sense.**

   a. Tim does not smoke. He is a _____ smoker.

   b. This cycle has three wheels. It is a _____ cycle.

   c. These goods are sent overseas. We _____ port them.

   d. We have put it off to a later date. We have _____ poned it.

   e. The groceries cost too much. They have _____ charged me.

   f. We are going shopping in that large shop. It is a _____ market.

   g. I am not sure who he is. I am _____ certain of his name.

   h. They are not paying me enough. I am _____ paid.

From Time-Savers for Teachers: Spelling Years 5-6. This page may be reproduced for classroom use.

65

Prefixes and Suffixes

Name _____

1. **Add or or er to the end of each word.**

   a. She listened to the song on the transist_____ radio.

   b. The bank tell_____ gave me ten pounds.

   c. Our refrigerat_____ keeps our drinks cold all day.

   d. The propell_____ on the old plane was made of wood.

   e. The act_____ was applauded for his performance.

   f. Our teach_____ read us a story about a lost dog.

   g. The divis_____ is fifteen.

   h. The lady standing over there is a foreign_____.

2. **Match each word with its definition.**

   a. a storyteller   inventor

   b. a person who invents   sculptor

   c. a writer of stories   surveyor

   d. a person who carves stone   author

   e. a person who flies a plane   narrator

   f. a person who measures angles   aviator

3. **Add a suffix to complete the word and the sentence.**

   a. That was a most enjoy_____ walk. (able ible)

   b. This is the clean_____ room in the house. (ist est)

   c. We are hope_____ he will arrive soon. (ful full)

   d. Sally is a very reli_____ student. (able ible)

   e. Mike is a sens_____ person. (able ible)

   f. Gunpowder is an explos_____ substance. (ist ive)

   g. From here the bridge is clearly vis_____. (ible able)

Prefixes and Suffixes

Name _____

1. Words can be broken down into different parts: the *prefix*, the *base* and the *suffix*. Put the word parts in order to make a word that matches the definition.

			prefix → base → suffix
a.	employ ed un	having no work	**un employ ed**
b.	ible in vis	not able to be seen	_____
c.	agree ment dis	dispute	_____
d.	appear dis ing	going out of sight	_____
e.	mark able re	out of the ordinary	_____
f.	arm dis ed	having no weapons	_____
g.	behave mis d	behaved badly	_____
h.	joint dis ed	not connected well	_____

2. Add the prefixes **in**, **im**, **il**, **ir**, **non**, **mis** to make each of these words its opposite.
   e.g. visible = invisible

   a. ____understand   e. ____responsible   i. ____literate   m. ____rational

   b. ____legal   f. ____possible   j. ____spell   n. ____polite

   c. ____regular   g. ____sane   k. ____patient   o. ____metal

   d. ____fortune   h. ____smoker   l. ____accurate   p. ____legible

3. Match each word to its correct definition.

   a. clearly different   distress

   b. worry, trouble   disrupt

   c. interfere with   discuss

   d. an illness   dissect

   e. to talk about something   distinct

   f. to cut to pieces   disease

From Time-Savers for Teachers: Spelling Years 5-6. This page may be reproduced for classroom use.

67

Prefixes and Suffixes

Name _____

1. **Complete each word.**

   Use these.

ace	ade	age	ate	are

   a. surf_____

   b. marmal_____

   c. chocol_____

   d. neckl_____

   e. clim_____

   f. investig_____

   g. grim_____

   h. mir_____

   i. seren_____

   j. prep_____

   k. lemon_____

   l. infiltr_____

2. **Complete each word.**

   Use these.

ure	ance	ary

   a. The train is **station**_____ on the line.

   b. We walked through the **entr**_____ to the building.

   c. My mother is a **secret**_____ for a publishing company.

   d. The **can**_____ was happy in its large cage.

   e. The **struct**_____ of the building was sound.

   f. Last week my parents celebrated their wedding **annivers**_____.

   g. The snails in our garden are a **nuis**_____ this year.

   h. We felt happy and **sec**_____ in the warmth of our beds.

3. **Complete each word with the correct suffix.**

   a. pian_____ (ist est) person who plays the piano

   b. humor_____ (ure ous) funny

   c. poss_____ (ible able) able to be done

   d. forg_____ (ery ary) illegal imitation

   e. gold_____ (an en) a gold colour

   f. explos_____ (ive ist) something that explodes

   g. hope_____ (ist less) without hope

   h. false_____ (hood ful) a lie

   i. length_____ (an en) make longer

   j. diction_____ (ery ary) book of word meanings

Prefixes and Suffixes

Name _____

1. **Write the base word. The first one has been done for you.**

    a. plentiful   **plenty**   f. meteorology _____

    b. reliability _____   g. happiness _____

    c. disappearing _____   h. foreigner _____

    d. buried _____   i. adulthood _____

    e. beautiful _____   j. courageous _____

2. **Add a prefix to complete each word so that the sentences make sense.**

    Use these.

out	in	fore	il	un	im	anti	inter

    a. This liquid kills germs. It is an _____septic.

    b. This is the front of my head. It is my _____head.

    c. She cannot read or write. She is _____literate.

    d. Jesse James lived outside the law. He was an _____law.

    e. This insect is not fully developed. It is still _____mature.

    f. Mr Jones is said to be quite mad. He is _____sane.

    g. The roads meet over there. We call it an _____section.

    h. John is not a well-liked boy. John is very _____popular.

3. **Break each word up into its prefix and base word, or base word and suffix.**
    e.g. unnecessary = un + necessary

    a. antifreeze = _____   g. convertible = _____

    b. illegal = _____   h. worthless = _____

    c. impatient = _____   i. foolish = _____

    d. interstellar = _____   j. actively = _____

    e. disallow = _____   k. successful = _____

    f. superhuman = _____   l. orphanage = _____

Prefixes and Suffixes

Name _____

1. **Make the word in brackets end in ed. Write the new word in the space.**

   a. Nick _____ all the way across the road. (hop)

   b. The hunter _____ the rabbit he had shot. (skin)

   c. I _____ up the dirty water on the floor. (mop)

   d. The car _____ at the red lights. (stop)

   e. The audience _____ loudly when she finished her act. (clap)

   f. The dog _____ the large bone across the lawn. (drag)

   g. We sat down and carefully _____ our camping expedition. (plan)

   h. The bees _____ loudly when the ants came near. (hum)

2. **Complete these lists. The first one has been done for you.**

	+ ed	+ ing			+ ed	+ ing
a. chop	**chopped**	**chopping**	f.	ban	_____	_____
b. rub	_____	_____	g.	flog	_____	_____
c. drop	_____	_____	h.	beg	_____	_____
d. step	_____	_____	i.	grip	_____	_____
e. map	_____	_____	j.	scrub	_____	_____

3. **Make the word in brackets end in ing. Write the word in the space.**

Rule: Final **e** goes away when **ing** comes to stay.

   a. I am **hoping** she arrives soon. (hope)

   b. They are _____ the signs on the door. (change)

   c. We are _____ the freshly cooked food. (taste)

   d. The dog is _____ the cat across the yard. (chase)

   e. Jack is _____ goodbye to his friends. (wave)

   f. I am _____ my money to buy a bike. (save)

   g. The stars are _____ brightly. (shine)

   h. We are going _____ in the countryside next week. (hike)

Prefixes and Suffixes

Name _____

1. **Make the word in brackets end in y. The first one has been done for you.**

   a. This is a ____**noisy**____ concert. (noise)

   b. We walked along the _____ path. (stone)

   c. This is a very _____ pie. (taste)

   d. We put more wood on the _____ fire. (smoke)

   e. The hedgehog has a _____ coat. (spike)

   f. Sally has dark, _____ hair. (wave)

2. **Complete these lists by adding the given letters. Remember to check your spellings.**

		+ s	+ ed	+ ing
a.	chop	_____	_____	_____
b.	clean	_____	_____	_____
c.	boast	_____	_____	_____
d.	paint	_____	_____	_____
e.	weed	_____	_____	_____
f.	rain	_____	_____	_____
g.	sprain	_____	_____	_____
h.	need	_____	_____	_____

3. **Make the word in brackets end in ly. Write the word in the space.**

   a. We walked _____ across the yard. (slow)

   b. The choir sang _____. (loud)

   c. The mouse ran _____ into its hole. (quick)

   d. The sun was shining _____. (bright)

   e. She spoke _____ to the new pupil. (nice)

   f. The model ship was only _____ completed. (part)

   g. We _____ said goodbye to our friends. (sad)

   h. The mother spoke _____ to the sobbing child. (soft)

Prefixes and Suffixes

Name _____

1. **Add ie or ei in the spaces.**

   > Rule: **i** before **e** except after **c** when the sound is **ee**.

   a. f____ld (paddock)

   b. n____ce (relation)

   c. c____ling (top of room)

   d. bel____ve (to think)

   e. tr____d (to have attempted)

   f. rec____ve (to be given)

   g. s____ve (a kitchen tool)

   h. cr____d (yelled)

   i. th____f (burglar)

   j. perc____ve (to see)

   k. p____ce (part of)

   l. ch____f (main person)

   m. fr____nd (mate)

   n. rec____pt (written docket for goods)

2. **Make each word in brackets end in ed.**

   a. The audience _____ at the end of the concert. (clap)

   b. The smuggler _____ the jewels to her body. (strap)

   c. Sun Yen _____ up the spilt water. (mop)

   d. I _____ right across the street. (hop)

   e. The dog _____ the bone in the garden. (bury)

   f. He _____ to cross the river unsuccessfully. (try)

   g. The baby _____ all morning. (cry)

   h. I _____ the dishes after James washed them. (dry)

3. **Make each of these words end in ing. Remember to check your spellings.**

   e.g. cry + ing = crying

   a. bury _____

   b. dine _____

   c. hope _____

   d. travel _____

   e. carry _____

   f. obey _____

   g. accompany _____

   h. marry _____

   i. worry _____

   j. injury _____

   k. refer _____

   l. occur _____

   m. fulfil _____

   n. traffic _____

   o. picnic _____

   p. age _____

Answers to Prefixes and Suffixes

Answers to page 64

1 change, wave, ice, taste, race, shake, shine, love, ride

2 hum, chop, clap, skip, map, step, skin, shop, rob

3 treatment, foolish, helpless, hopeful, sadness, slower, graceful, longest, sickness

Answers to page 65

1 unhappy, impossible, disobey, disappointing, unfair, disappear, impolite, unpack

2 exhibition, excursion, experiment, excavate, example

3 non-smoker, tricycle, export, postponed, overcharged, supermarket, uncertain, underpaid

Answers to page 66

1 transistor, teller, refrigerator, propeller, actor, teacher, divisor, foreigner

2 inventor, author, sculptor, aviator, surveyor

3 enjoyable, cleanest, hopeful, reliable, sensible, explosive, visible

Answers to page 67

1 invisible, disagreement, disappearing, remarkable, disarmed, misbehaved, disjointed

2 misunderstand, illegal, irregular, misfortune, irresponsible, impossible, insane, non-smoker, illiterate, mis-spell, impatient, inaccurate, irrational, impolite, non-metal, illegible

3 distinct, distress, disrupt, disease, discuss, dissect

Answers to page 68

1 surface, marmalade, chocolate, necklace, climate, investigate, grimace, mirage, serenade, prepare, lemonade, infiltrate

2 stationary, entrance, secretary, canary, structure, anniversary, nuisance, secure

3 pianist, humorous, possible, forgery, golden, explosive, hopeless, falsehood, lengthen, dictionary

Answers to page 69

1 rely, disappear, bury, beauty, meteor, happy, foreign, adult, courage

2 antiseptic, forehead, illiterate, outlaw, immature, insane, intersection, unpopular

3 anti + freeze, il + legal, im + patient, inter + stellar, dis + allow, super + human, convert + ible, worth + less, fool + ish, active + ly, success + ful, orphan + age

Answers to page 70

1 hopped, skinned, mopped, stopped, clapped, dragged, planned, hummed

2 rubbed, rubbing; dropped, dropping; stepped, stepping; mapped, mapping; banned, banning; flogged, flogging; begged, begging; gripped, gripping; scrubbed, scrubbing

3 changing, tasting, chasing, waving, saving, shining, hiking

Answers to page 71

1 stony, tasty, smoky, spiky, wavy

2 chops, chopped, chopping; cleans, cleaned, cleaning; boasts, boasted, boasting; paints, painted, painting; weeds, weeded, weeding; rains, rained, raining; sprains, sprained, spraining; needs, needed, needing

3 slowly, loudly, quickly, brightly, nicely, partly, sadly, softly

Answers to page 72

1 field, niece, ceiling, believe, tried, receive, sieve cried, thief, perceive, piece, chief, friend, receipt

2 clapped, strapped, mopped, hopped, buried, tried, cried, dried

3 burying, dining, hoping, travelling, carrying, obeying, accompanying, marrying, worrying, injuring, referring, occurring, fulfilling, trafficking, picnicking, ageing

Introduction to Common Errors

This section is about strategies for editing, correcting and polishing one's own work, using a variety of techniques. The National Literacy Strategy suggests:

Y5T3 W1: to identify mis-spelt words in own writing; to keep individual lists (e.g. spelling logs); to learn to spell them;

Y5T3 W2: to use known spellings as a basis for spelling other words with similar patterns or related meanings;

Y5T3 W3: to use independent spelling strategies, including:

- building up spellings by syllabic parts, using known prefixes, suffixes and common letter strings;

- applying knowledge of spelling rules and exceptions;

- building words from other known words, and from awareness of the meaning or derivations of words;

- using dictionaries and IT spell-checks;

- using visual skills, e.g. recognising common letter strings and checking critical features (i.e. does it look right, shape, length, etc.).

Copy the grid on page 95 for each pupil to make their personal list of common errors.

Common Errors

Name _____

1. *Find the mistake.*   One vowel has been used incorrectly in each word.
   Write each word correctly.

   a. villige   _____

   b. seperate   _____

   c. serprised   _____

   d. docter   _____

   e. distroy   _____

   f. propellor   _____

   g. computor   _____

   h. definate   _____

   i. cotten   _____

   j. bisiness   _____

2. A letter has been left out of each of these words. Write each word correctly.

   a. adress   _____

   b. traveler   _____

   c. begining   _____

   d. safty   _____

   e. evry   _____

   f. goverment   _____

   g. jewelery   _____

   h. libary   _____

   i. disapeared   _____

   j. receit   _____

3. A letter has been wrongly added to each of these words.
   Write the word correctly.

   a. beautifull   _____

   b. burgular   _____

   c. umberella   _____

   d. addmittance   _____

   e. untill   _____

   f. allways   _____

   g. useing   _____

   h. comeing   _____

   i. truely   _____

   j. filim   _____

Common Errors

Name _____

1. **Choose the correctly spelt word to complete each sentence.**

   a. From here the spires of the church are _____. (visible   visable)

   b. I walked from the back to the _____ of the room. (front   frount)

   c. It is _____ seven o'clock. (almost   allmost)

   d. Maxine wrote her friend's _____ on the envelope. (adress   address)

   e. We cut the paper with a pair of _____. (sissors   scissors)

   f. We must wait here _____ he comes. (until   untill)

   g. I put a spoonful of _____ in my drink. (suger   sugar)

   h. I tried to _____ the fighting cats. (separate   seperate)

2. **Circle the correct spelling of each word. Write the word.**

   a. they _____

   thay

   b. hurt _____

   hert

   c. cotten _____

   cotton

   d. docter _____

   doctor

   e. library _____

   libary

   f. meny _____

   many

   g. orful _____

   awful

   h. evry _____

   every

   i. becorse _____

   because

3. **Find eight words in the grid.**

u	s	e	f	u	l	a
m	f	j	t	g	g	l
i	o	e	r	u	u	w
g	r	w	u	e	a	a
h	t	e	l	s	r	y
t	y	l	y	s	d	s

   _____   _____

   _____   _____

   _____   _____

   _____   _____

Common Errors

Name _____

1. **Write the correct spelling of the word to complete the sentence.**

   a. It is the _____ day of May today. (**eigth**).

   b. The boys ran to the _____ of the house. (**safty**)

   c. This shirt is made of _____. (**cotten**)

   d. Ravi _____ does his best work in class. (**allways**)

   e. The rose is a _____ flower. (**beautifull**)

   f. Next _____ our class is going on an excursion. (**Wensday**)

   g. I saw Joanne _____ to school. (**comeing**)

   h. Our _____ has over five hundred students. (**skool**)

2. **Circle, then write the correct spelling of each word.**

   a. allmost _____
   almost

   b. using _____
   useing

   c. hopeing _____
   hoping

   d. welcom _____
   welcome

   e. seperate _____
   separate

   f. droped _____
   dropped

   g. climed _____
   climbed

   h. answer _____
   anser

   i. minit _____
   minute

3. **In these words a letter is missing. Write the words correctly.**

   a. jewelery _____

   b. traveler _____

   c. disapear _____

   d. carrage _____

   e. ocasion _____

   f. goverment _____

4. **In these words a letter has been added. Write the words correctly.**

   a. comeing _____

   b. burgular _____

   c. athaletics _____

   d. begginning _____

   e. addmittance _____

   f. umberella _____

Common Errors

Name _____

1. **Circle the correct spelling.**

   a. The belt is made of goat skin (leather lether).

   b. Can you do that (agian again) for me?

   c. We put a spoonful of (suger sugar) in her tea.

   d. I (thort thought) we would be there by now.

   e. The teacher said "I'd like to (welcom welcome) you here."

   f. There were a lot of (peeple people) at the zoo.

   g. The children are (runing running) across the yard.

   h. Chris is a (bright brite) and happy boy.

2. **The incorrect homophones have been used in this story. Rewrite the story using the correct homophones.**

   One day a large **bare** found a **bury** tree growing in the **would**. With its large **pause** it pulled a **bow** of the tree **write** down **too** the ground. It **eight** all the fruit then went to the **creak four** a drink. Just then it **herd** the **raw** of a large **bore** searching for food. It was the same pig the bear had **scene** only **for** days ago searching **threw** the **waist** left by careless campers.

   _____

   _____

   _____

   _____

   _____

   _____

   _____

   _____

3. **Circle the correct spelling.**

a.	laugh	laff	**f.**	messige message
b.	dream	dreem	**g.**	stable stabel
c.	middel	middle	**h.**	picked pickt
d.	allmost	almost	**i.**	office ofice
e.	factory	factry	**j.**	welcome welcom

Common Errors

Name _____

1. **The passage contains twelve spelling errors. Underline them. Write the passage correctly.**

   That nite, when it was dark, thay quietly crept allong and got on the ship's deck. Evryone was two busy to notice them. By and by they came to a blak, sqare hole, and down they crept by a lader that was in it. They found a lower deck affter they had gone down a littel way, and had just steped onto it when the hole was coverred over. (from *Rags and Tatters*)

   _____

   _____

   _____

   _____

   _____

   _____

   _____

   _____

   _____

2. **Look at this picture and underline the spelling errors. Write the words correctly.**

Kemist

J. Jones

We sell all your cosmetic needs —

lipstiks,

face powda

Jewelry

M. Smith

New waches for sail

25% off daimond rings

Greengrocer

cabage	50p
cukumber	75p
letuce	90p
tomatos	95p

   _____

   _____

Common Errors

Name _____

1. Underline all the spelling errors, then write the story correctly.

The cheif took a white feather from one of his arows and stuk it firmly over the center of the roof in a peculier way. "With that white feather above you're house," he said to Robert Wisbot, "your settlement is safe. We Indians are your freinds hence forward and you are ours."

Nothing more was said; and a few momments later the strange gests, with there weapons in their hands, had all dissapeared as noiselessly as thay had come. (from *The Feather*, July 1996)

_____

_____

_____

_____

_____

_____

_____

2. Read this menu carefully. Underline all the spelling errors.

Soup of the Day	Pumkin soup with tost
Entrees	Seefood cocktale Chicken liver paté Smoked sallmon
Main Courses	Medium roast of beef and hoase raddish suace Leg of lam and mint sauce
Salads	Coleslaw and potatoe salad Pasta salad with mushrooms
Deserts	Chocolate mouse Appel strudel Chesecake
Beverages	Cofee and tea

Common Errors

Name _____

1. Underline all the spelling errors in the recipe.

Pinappel Stake

Ingrediants

1 kilogram stake cut into six peices
1 spoonfull of vegetabble oil

Sauce: 1 liter of juice from a can of pineapple
       1 spoonfull of honey
       1 spoonful of lemmon juice
       1 onoin, chopped
       salt and peper

Place oil in verry hot pan and brown stake litely on both sides. Place in buttered casserole dish.

Make the sauce by placing all ingredients in a saucpan. Bring to the boil and pore over steaks. Cover and bake at 200°C for 10 minutes, reducing heat to 180°C for 1 hour. Remove any fat from sauce and thicken with a littel blended flouer. Add extra stock is nessessary. Serve with bakked jacked potatos and sliced coocked carotts.

---

2. Circle the correct spelling of each word.

a.	captain	captian	f.	picnic	picnick
b.	holaday	holiday	g.	travel	travell
c.	botom	bottom	h.	tunnle	tunnel
d.	because	becorse	i.	enuff	enough
e.	wonderfull	wonderful	j.	forty	fourty

Common Errors

Name _____

1. In the grid there are eight words with four letters. Each word contains a silent letter. Find each word and complete each sentence.

c	b	o	m	b	h
o	h	a	l	f	o
m	c	a	l	f	u
b	y	o	l	k	r
x	a	c	h	e	x
x	x	k	n	i	t

   a. Two quarters make one _____.

   b. A young cow is called a _____.

   c. I have a tooth _____.

   d. The _____ exploded in the street.

   e. There are sixty minutes in one _____.

   f. I tidied my hair with a _____.

   g. The yellow part of an egg is called the _____.

   h. I like to _____ my own woollen socks.

2. Write the word that contains a silent letter. Circle the silent letter.

   a. paper   sword   book   _____

   b. island   sheet   table   _____

   c. answer   grass   sand   _____

   d. folder   balloon   depot   _____

   e. doubt   library   line   _____

   f. cover   tape   scissors   _____

   g. ruin   wreck   bold   _____

   h. scheme   plan   atlas   _____

3. Each word in the box contains a silent letter. Write each word beside its definition.

   Use these words.

wrist	wren	dinghy	whole
tomb	choir	hymn	gnat
beret	knuckle	kneel	rhubarb

   a. small insect   _____

   b. small bird   _____

   c. group of singers   _____

   d. joint of the hand and arm   _____

   e. a grave   _____

   f. a type of soft cap   _____

   g. a religious song   _____

   h. a small boat   _____

   i. joint of the finger   _____

   j. entire   _____

   k. a plant   _____

   l. to rest on the knees   _____

Common Errors

Name _____

1. **Ten words in the grid contain a silent letter. Write each word on a line and circle the silent letter.**

h	y	m	n	s	k	w	w
t	g	d	k	c	n	r	h
h	n	e	n	i	u	a	i
u	o	p	e	e	c	p	s
m	m	o	a	n	k	p	t
b	e	t	d	c	l	e	l
w	r	e	n	e	e	r	e

_____   _____

_____   _____

_____   _____

_____   _____

_____   _____

2. Each word in the box contains a silent letter. Write each word beside its link word.

answer	hymn	schedule	beret	island
wriggle	knitting	thumb	gnash	tomb

a. timetable _____
b. needles _____
c. cap _____
d. grave _____
e. worm _____

f. teeth _____
g. question _____
h. church _____
i. finger _____
j. continent _____

3. **Complete each sentence.**

Use these words.

scheme	handsome	knuckle	chemical
rhyme	symptom	wreath	pneumatic

a. Ammonia can sometimes be a dangerous _____.
b. Words such as hair and bare _____.
c. We laid a _____ at the cenotaph.
d. He hurt his _____ when he hit the door.
e. The film star is said to be a most _____ man.
f. Red spots on the skin is a _____ of measles.
g. Our class developed a clever _____ to raise money for the charity.
h. The workers dug up the road using _____ drills.

Common Errors

Some words are often spelt incorrectly. The words below have been classified into common errors that occur. Try to learn as many of these spellings as you can!

Words in which the wrong vowel is often used:

awful	destroy	tailor	regular	doctor
imposter	anchor	symptom	cotton	sugar
business	system	definite	separate	front
propeller	visible	village	because	they
hurt	surface	many	governor	surprised
minute	wanted			

Words from which letters are often deleted:

address	every	afford	ascend	beautiful
aeroplane	accommodation	beginning	biggest	carriage
committee	cupboard	disappeared	eighth	except
edge	dyeing	singeing	forgetting	jewellery
jealous	receipt	swimming	woollen	safely
traveller	useful	referred	quarrelling	safety
guarantee	February	library	Wednesday	disappoint
admittance	occasion	climbed	school	ladies
judge	escape	ache	guess	answer
guard	exhibit	picture	different	interest
might	dropped			

Words in which letters are often added:

admittance	almost	always	until	attached
bachelor	balance	beautiful	spoonful	plentiful
beginning	burglar	buried	coming	film
fulfil	hoping	forty	lightning	mistaken
movable	necessary	pastime	quarrelsome	jewel
shining	skilful	trespass	truly	front
umbrella	using	welcome	wooden	aquarium
which				

Answers to Common Errors

Answers to page 75

1 village, separate, surprised, doctor, destroy, propeller, computer, definite, cotton, business

2 address, traveller, beginning, safety, every, government, jewellery, library, disappeared, receipt

3 beautiful, burglar, umbrella, admittance, until, always, using, coming, truly, film

Answers to page 76

1 visible, front, almost, address, scissors, until, sugar, separate

2 they, hurt, cotton, doctor, library, many, awful, every, because

3 useful, might, forty, jewel, truly, guess, guard, always

Answers to page 77

1 eighth, safety, cotton, always, beautiful, Wednesday, coming, school

2 almost, using, hoping, welcome, separate, dropped, climbed, answer, minute

3 jewellery, traveller, disappear, carriage, occasion, government

4 coming, burglar, athletics, beginning, admittance, umbrella

Answers to page 78

1 leather, again, sugar, thought, welcome, people, running, bright

2 bear, berry, wood, paws, bough, right, to, ate, creek, for, heard, roar, boar, seen, four, through, waste

3 laugh, dream, middle, almost, factory, message, stable, picked, office, welcome

Answers to page 79

1 night, they, along, Everyone, too, black, square, ladder, after, little, stepped, covered

2 Chemist, lipsticks, powder

Jewellery, watches, sale, diamond

cabbage, cucumber lettuce, tomatoes

Answers to page 80

1 chief, arrows, stuck, centre, peculiar, your, friends, moments, guests, their, disappeared, they

2 Pumpkin, toast, Seafood, cocktail,

salmon, horse, radish, sauce, lamb, potato, Desserts, mousse, Apple, Cheesecake, Coffee

Answers to page 81

1 Pineapple, Steak, Ingredients, steak, pieces, spoonful, vegetable, litre, spoonful, lemon, onion, pepper, very, steak, lightly, saucepan, pour, little, flour, as, necessary, baked, jacket, potatoes, cooked, carrots

2 captain, holiday, bottom, because, wonderful, picnic, travel, tunnel, enough, forty

Answers to page 82

1 half, calf, ache, bomb, hour, comb, yolk, knit

2 sword, island, answer, depot, doubt, scissors, wreck, scheme

3 gnat, wren, choir, wrist, tomb, beret, hymn, dinghy, knuckle, whole, rhubarb, kneel

Answers to page 83

1 depot, gnome, hymn, knead, knuckle, science, thumb, whistle, wrapper, wren

2 schedule, knitting, beret, tomb, wriggle, gnash, answer, hymn, thumb, island

3 chemical, rhyme, wreath, knuckle, handsome, symptom, scheme, pneumatic

Introduction and Answers to New Words

The National Literacy Strategy uses its Vocabulary extension sections to recommend that pupils look at word derivations, and collect words from new sources:

Y5T3 W8: to identify everyday words such as spaghetti, bungalow, boutique which have been borrowed from other languages, and to understand how this might give clues to spelling;

Y5T3 W10: to understand how words can be formed from longer words, e.g. through the omission of letters – o'clock, Hallowe'en; through omission of prefixes – (omni)bus, (tele)phone, (aero)plane; through the use of acronyms – radar, CD;

Y6T1 W 9: to understand how new words have been added to the language, e.g. trainers, wheelie.

Answers to page 87

1 spam, hydrofoil, nylon, Chunnel, modem, flip-flops, radar, supersonic

2 scuba, rayon, periscope, microwave, software, monorail, microsurgery, laminex

Answers to page 88

1 gymnasium, afternoon, bicycle, television, ammunition, examination, hippopotamus, doctor, telephone, photographs

2a holidays, football, sandwiches, training shoes

b bricklayer, barbecue, presents, potatoes, mosquitoes

Answers to page 89

1 petrol, holiday, rubbish, biscuit, autumn, car, lift, tap, frying-pan, chemist or pharmacist

2 napkin, apartment, janitor, closet, zip-code, oatmeal, cracker, candy, trashcan, jelly

3 grey, pyjamas, metre, centre, traveller, axe

New Words

Name _____

1. **Match each word in the box to its meaning below.**

modem	spam	nylon	supersonic
flip-flops	hydrofoil	Chunnel	radar

   a. unwanted emails or text messages _____

   b. a boat that can travel above the surface of the water _____

   c. a type of material _____

   d. the tunnel linking England and France _____

   e. a device to connect computers _____

   f. a type of footwear _____

   g. a radio tracking system _____

   h. faster than the speed of sound _____

2. **Complete each sentence.**

rayon	microwave	laminex	software
microsurgery	periscope	scuba	monorail

   a. We are going _____ diving next week.

   b. The shirt is made of a mixture of _____ and wool.

   c. The commander of the submarine ordered the _____ raised.

   d. We reheated the pasta in the _____.

   e. Our school purchased some new _____ for the computers.

   f. We travelled around the fun-park on a _____.

   g. His severed fingers were attached by _____.

   h. The table top was covered with _____.

3. **Use a dictionary to help you write the meaning of each of these words.**

   a. microwave _____

   b. commuter _____

   c. disco _____

   d. launderette _____

New Words

Name _____

1. **Write the full word for each underlined shortening.**

   a. At lunchtime I worked out in the <u>gym</u>. _____

   b. What are you doing this <u>p.m.</u>? _____

   c. Mike rode his new <u>bike</u> to school. _____

   d. Did you watch the news on <u>telly</u> last night? _____

   e. The hunter grabbed a handful of <u>ammo</u> from the box. _____

   f. How did you do in the Maths <u>exam</u>? _____

   g. A <u>hippo</u> is often called a river horse. _____

   h. I have to see the <u>doc</u>. _____

   i. I'll call you on the <u>phone</u> tonight. _____

   j. We took some <u>photos</u> of the school fete. _____

2. **Rewrite the passages replacing the shortenings with the correct word.**

   a. During the <u>hols</u>, when my uncle went to the <u>footy</u> he took half a dozen <u>sarnies</u> and wore his <u>trainers</u>.

   _____

   _____

   _____

   b. Mr Smith, who is a <u>brickie</u>, invited us to a <u>barbie</u> at his home for his birthday. After the <u>pressies</u> had been given out we cooked some <u>spuds</u> and burgers. However, the <u>mozzies</u> were so bad we had to go inside.

   _____

   _____

   _____

   _____

New Words

Name _____

1. **Replace the underlined American word with the English word.**

    a. My mother filled the car with <u>gasoline</u>. _____

    b. Are you going away during the Christmas <u>vacation</u>? _____

    c. The class put the <u>trash</u> in the bin. _____

    d. I ate a chocolate <u>cookie</u> at lunch time. _____

    e. During the <u>fall</u> the weather becomes cooler. _____

    f. The stolen <u>automobile</u> was pursued by the police. _____

    g. We travelled to the next floor in the <u>elevator</u>. _____

    h. The plumber mended the leaking <u>faucet</u>. _____

    i. We fried the meat in the <u>skillet</u>. _____

    j. I bought some cosmetics from the <u>druggist</u>. _____

2. **Rewrite each sentence on a separate sheet of paper, replacing the underlined word with the American term from the box.**

cracker	apartment	oatmeal	janitor	closet
napkin	zip-code	candy	trashcan	jelly

    a. I wiped my mouth with a <u>serviette</u>.

    b. His <u>flat</u> is in the city.

    c. The <u>cleaner</u> put the papers in the bin.

    d. I hung my clothes neatly in the <u>cupboard</u>.

    e. I wrote the <u>postcode</u> on the envelope.

    f. I like to eat <u>porridge</u> for breakfast.

    g. I spread some butter on the <u>biscuit</u>.

    h. It is unwise to eat a lot of <u>sweets</u>.

    i. The <u>bin</u> is overflowing with papers.

    j. I spread <u>jam</u> on the slice of bread.

3. **Write how we spell the following words.**

    a. gray _____
    b. pajamas _____
    c. meter _____

    d. center _____
    e. traveler _____
    f. ax _____

From Time-Savers for Teachers: Spelling Years 5-6. This page may be reproduced for classroom use.

89

Introduction and Answers to Word Fun

This section includes further worksheets to consolidate some of the spelling strategies covered in the book, and have some fun with words!

Answers to page 91

1 honey, dozen, silver, basket, bottom, leather, crayon, million, volcano, wizard

2 together, yesterday, telephone, surrounded, conversation, beginning, circular, somersault, handkerchief, generator

3 fish, fall; does, dish; game, glow; food, hear; flag, hair; left, nose; once, path; rock, stay; grew, tent; duck, flat

Answers to page 92

1 knives, shark, marry, jelly, bottle, spear, soap, shave, scream, pullet

2 lamb, eagle, crocodile, trumpet, bicycle, sugar, million or billion, question, blanket, banana

3 hamburger, potato, present, rooster, yellow, mosquitoes, pyjamas, rhinoceros, swallow, toadstool

Answers to page 93

1 falcon, chapel, fountain, glutton, lettuce, oyster, pigeon, rooster, circle, weather

2 entertainment, educational, environment, hippopotamus, indigestion, thermometer

3 gallop, fiddle; nugget, middle; pigeon, rattle; turnip, vanish; bridge, square; insect, kitten

Answers to page 94

1 nightingale, generation, ashamed, combination, exclamation, prototype, together

2 escaped, concluded, entertain, separate, encourage, cabinet, disaster, companion

3 pelican, kennel, yellow, lizard, willow, venison, guitar, peach, cabbage, abacus

Word Fun

Name _____

1. **Rearrange the jumbled letters to make a word that matches the definition.**

   a. hnoey (bees make it) _____

   b. zdnoe (twelve) _____

   c. liserv (metal) _____

   d. baskte (container) _____

   e. bttmoo (opposite of top) _____

   f. tlherae (tanned hide of animals) _____

   g. ncraoy (writing implement) _____

   h. limlnio (large number) _____

   i. ovcalon (exploding mountain) _____

   j. iwzard (magician) _____

2. **Join the word pieces to make a larger word.**

   a. to+get+her = _____

   b. yes+ter+day = _____

   c. tel+e+phone = _____

   d. su+rr+ounded = _____

   e. con+ver+sation = _____

   f. be+gin+ning = _____

   g. circ+u+lar = _____

   h. som+er+sault = _____

   i. hand+ker+chief = _____

   j. gen+er+ator = _____

3. **Join the letter pairs to make two words.**

   e.g. fo be ur ar **four bear**

   a. fi fa sh ll _____ _____

   b. do di sh es _____ _____

   c. ga me gl ow _____ _____

   d. od fo he ar _____ _____

   e. fl ha ir ag _____ _____

   f. le no se ft _____ _____

   g. ce on th pa _____ _____

   h. ay ro st ck _____ _____

   i. te gr nt ew _____ _____

   j. at du ck fl _____ _____

Word Fun

92

Name _____

1. **Change one letter to make a word that matches the definition.**

   a. knaves (cutting implements) _____   f. smear (a weapon) _____

   b. shirk (large fish) _____   g. soup (we wash with it) _____

   c. merry (wed) _____   h. shape (to remove hair) _____

   d. jolly (sweet dessert) _____   i. stream (to yell loudly) _____

   e. battle (glass container) _____   j. bullet (a young fowl) _____

2. **The first two letters of each word are missing. Complete each word.**

   a. _ _ mb (young sheep)   f. _ _ gar (sweetener)

   b. _ _ gle (bird of prey)   g. _ _ llion (large number)

   c. _ _ ocodile (reptile)   h. _ _ estion (opposite to answer)

   d. _ _ umpet (musical instrument)   i. _ _ anket (bed covering)

   e. _ _ cycle (two-wheeled vehicle)   j. _ _ nana (fruit)

3. **The first three letters of each word are missing. Complete each word.**

   a. _ _ _ burger (take away food)   f. _ _ _ quitoes (insects)

   b. _ _ _ ato (vegetable)   g. _ _ _ amas (nightwear)

   c. _ _ _ sent (gift)   h. _ _ _ noceros (large animal)

   d. _ _ _ ster (male fowl)   i. _ _ _ llow (small bird)

   e. _ _ _ low (colour)   j. _ _ _ dstool (fungus)

Word Fun

Name _____

1. **Rearrange the jumbled letters. Make a word that matches the definition.**

   a. alfcon (bird of prey) _____   f. tyoser (shellfish) _____

   b. ahcpel (small church) _____   g. gpeoin (bird) _____

   c. aofuntin (water spout) _____   h. toroser (male fowl)

   d. olguttn (person who eats too much)   _____
      _____   i. cicrle (round shape) _____

   e. uelttce (leafy vegetable) _____   j. eawethr (climate) _____

2. **Join the word pieces to make a larger word.**

   a. enter + tain + ment   = _____

   b. educat + ion + al   = _____

   c. envir + on + ment   = _____

   d. hippo + pot + amus   = _____

   e. in + digest + ion   = _____

   f. therm + o + meter   = _____

3. **Join the word pieces to make two words. Write each beside its definition.**

   a. gal fid dle lop
      move like a horse   _____
      violin   _____

   b. dle get nug mid
      piece of gold   _____
      centre   _____

   c. pig tle rat eon
      bird   _____
      baby's toy   _____

   d. tur ish nip van
      root vegetable   _____
      disappear   _____

   e. are squ dge bri
      span across a river   _____
      shape   _____

   f. ins ten kit ect
      six-legged creature   _____
      young cat   _____

Word Fun

Name _____

1. **Make words by joining word pieces from rows A, B and C. One has been done for you.**

A	B	C	
(perm)	in	ation	_permanent_
night	am	ation	_____
gen	to	ed	_____
ash	er	gale	_____
comb	get	type	_____
ex	in	her	_____
pro	(an)	ation	_____
to	clam	(ent)	_____
			_____

2. **Make a word that matches the definition.**

   a. cap es ed   got away   _____

   b. ded con clu   ended   _____

   c. tain ter en   to amuse   _____

   d. ate ar sep   not joined   _____

   e. age en cour   to give praise   _____

   f. cab et in   type of cupboard   _____

   g. as dis ter   terrible happening   _____

   h. ion pan com   someone with you   _____

3. **Complete each word. Use three letters.**

   a. peli_ _ _   bird   f. veni_ _ _   meat of a deer

   b. _ _ _nel   dog's home   g. gui_ _ _   stringed instrument

   c. _ _ _low   colour   h. pe_ _ _   fruit

   d. liz_ _ _   reptile   i. cabb_ _ _   leafy green vegetable

   e. wil_ _ _   type of tree   j. _ _ _cus   counting frame

94

From Time-Savers for Teachers: Spelling Years 5-6. This page may be reproduced for classroom use.

Checklist

Name _____

Record words you are having difficulty with on this page.

WORD	WORD	WORD

Index